THE NON ROTATIVE BEAM ENGINE

A monograph concerning the history of,
and technical information on,
the NEWCOMEN, the BOULTON & WATT
and the CORNISH engines

by

MAURICE KELLY

Member of the Newcomen Society.
Formerly: 2nd Engineer Officer, Royal Research Service & British Merchant Navy.
Chief Engineer Officer, Marina Mercante de Republica de Panama.

Camden Miniature
Steam Services.

Previous Works by the Author:

"The Overtype Steam Road Waggon"
Goose & Son Publishers, Norwich. 1971.

"The Undertype Steam Road Waggon"
Goose & Son Publishers, Cambridge. 1975

"The American Steam Traction Engine"
CMS Publishing, Stamford. 1995

British Library Cataloguing-in-Publication-Data: a catalogue record of this book is held by the British Library.

First Printing 2002

ISBN No. 0-9536523-3-5

Published in Great Britain by:

CAMDEN MINIATURE STEAM SERVICES
Barrow Farm, Rode, Frome, Somerset. BA11 6PS

Camden stock one of the widest selections of engineering, technical and transportation books to be found;
Write to the above address for a copy of their latest free Booklist.

Layout and Design by Camden Studios and Andrew Luckhurst, Trowbridge, Wilts.

Printed and Bound by Salisbury Printing Co. Ltd.

Front Cover Illustration:

The top nozzles of the ROBINSON 80 inch Cornish Engine at the South Crofty Mine in Cornwall.
After a painting by Terence Cuneo.
Reproduced by kind permission of the Cuneo Estate & Cuneo Fine Arts

Rear Cover Illustrations:

Top - Tinted engraving of an unidentified 60" Cornish Engine.
Reproduced by kind permission of the Editor of The Engineer

Bottom - "THE GIANT GRASSHOPPER" engine preserved at the Shore Road Pumping Station
by the Metropolitan Borough of the Wirral.
Photograph courtesy of the Metropolitan Borough of Wigan

CONTENTS

ACKNOWLEDGEMENTS

The Author would like to thank the following, and any he may have inadvertently missed, for their assistance in the preparation of this book.

LESLEY BOSSINE, Manager, Kew Bridge Steam Museum, and her team, for advice, help and reading the proofs.

PAUL CARSLAKE, Editor of the "ENGINEER" for permission to reproduce line drawings in the work.

HELOISE CATES, for setting up the typescript and storing it on disk on computer.

IAN COLES, Head of Libraries, Museums and Arts, Metropolitan Borough of Wirral.

JOHN CROMPTON, Curator of Engineering & Industry, National Museums of Scotland, Edinburgh. Information on NEWCOMEN engines etc. in their collection.

MIKE HARDING, Assistant Curator, Mechanical Engineering at the National Museum of Science & Industry, the Science Museum at South Kensington, London. Information and details concerning the engines and artefacts contained in the National Collection.

STEPHEN HOWARD, Curator at the Black Country Museum. Information on the preserved blowing engine at Aston and details of the Museum's replica of the 1712 Newcomen engine.

SAM JOHNSTONE, The Cornwall Record Office, for permission to include drawings in the work.

M. JEWKES, Curator of Scientific Instruments at the Hunterian Museum, University of Glasgow for information about artefacts concerning JAMES WATT in their collection.

R. SIMMONS, The Crofton Society, for information concerning the engines managed by the KENNNET & AVON CANAL TRUST and for permission to reproduce his drawings in the text.

Thanks are due to the Patent Office staff, the British Library and the Bank of England Archive Department.

Thanks are also due to NICHOLAS KELLY for encouragement and assistance with the compilation of the work.

The tinted drawing on the cover, and most of the line drawings are taken from the "ENGINEER" with the permission of the Editor.

Fig. 1. The Hawkesbury Junction Engine was drawn by the late Dr. C. T. G. BOUCHER and the copyright is held by the NEWCOMEN SOCIETY.

The Drawings of the PENTRICH and the ELSECAR Engines were drawn by the late CLARENCE O. SECKER M.Inst.M.E.

All other drawings are taken from various 18th & 19th Century sources as listed in the Bibliography.

CHAPTER 1: INTRODUCTION

The object of this monograph is to introduce the reader to a review of the history and to provide basic descriptions of the design and operation of the non-rotative beam engine from its inception during the early part of the 18th Century when the original 'Atmospheric' engine was invented by *THOMAS NEWCOMEN*, to its refinement in the form of the CORNISH engine which persisted in use into the first half of the 20th Century. The fact that a number of these engines have survived into preservation and are available for inspection by the general public gives rise for a need to present a concise report devoted to the technicalities of the three broad types, viz., the NEWCOMEN, the BOULTON & WATT and the CORNISH engines, together with some documentation concerning those examples which still exist and their locations in the United Kingdom.

Whilst there is no need in this publication to go into the convoluted histories of progenitors such as *THOMAS NEWCOMEN, JAMES WATT* and others, it is necessary to establish a degree of background to understand the relevance of the remaining engines that have been preserved as historical monuments. The careers of the early inventors and the machines that they built have been the subject of numerous books, pamphlets and articles over a period of some 200 years and the most important of these are recorded in the Bibliography at the end of this text.

The origins of the non-rotative steam pumping engine are to be found in the necessity to drain mines on the boundary of the 17th and the 18th Centuries; as mines were worked out at their upper levels, shafts were sunk to greater depths to exploit continuing veins of ore, and this activity brought the perennial danger of flooding the deep workings, which then became unstable. The first inventor to address the problem of flooded mines was Captain *THOMAS SAVERY* who came from a family of prosperous merchants in Totnes in Devon; his title of 'Captain' is enigmatic and may have been bestowed upon him as being an engineer in the Cornish Metal mines. He became a Fellow of the Royal Society in 1705 and is noted for his master patent for equipment to drain mines, British Patent No. 356 of the 25th July 1698, which remained in force, after extensions were applied for it, until 1733. In this patent SAVERY described his invention as being an apparatus for "raising water by the elasticity of steam – forming a vacuum by condensing steam to raise water by the

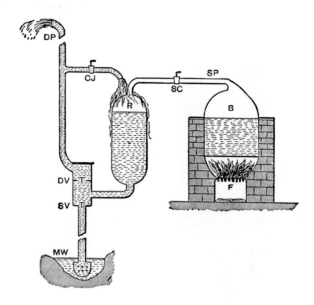

F	for	Furnace.	**M W**	for	Mine water.
B	,,	Boiler.	**S V**	,,	Suction valve.
S P	,,	Steam pipe.	**D V**	,,	Delivery valve.
S C	,,	Steam cock.	**C J**	,,	Condensing jet.
R	,,	Receiver.	**D P**	,,	Discharge pipe.

Diagram A - Savery's Engine of 1698 - Working principle.

pressure of the atmosphere". The fact that *SAVERY* had managed to protect an invention which had all the factors to build a proper steam engine and no one could involve themselves in such an endeavour without application to him, makes him the cornerstone of the steam revolution.

SAVERY's system employed boilers, valves and receivers and did not have any moveable components. It worked on the principles of differing pressures and vacuums which enabled chambers at lower levels to be emptied and the water to be discharged to higher locations. DIAGRAM 'A' shows the method utilised to achieve this end and the system operated in the following manner: Steam was raised in the boiler at **B** and this steam was conducted along the steam pipe **SP** to a receiver at **R** with the flow being controlled by means of a cock at **SC**. The engineman allowed the receiver to fill with steam and then shut off the steam cock **SC**: at this point another valve controlling the condensing jet of water **CJ** was opened and the resulting rush of cold water on the outside surface of the receiver caused the steam inside to condense. With the steam in the receiver condensed into water the vacuum caused thereby pulled open a Suction Valve **SV** and closed a Delivery Valve **DV** in an ancillary chamber

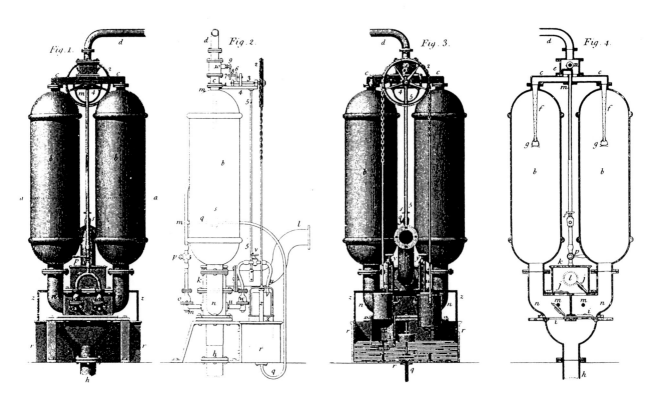

Fig. 1 - Drawings of the improved Savery pumping engine supplied to the City Gas Works in London by J. Pontifex in 1822.

connected to the receiver. The vacuum then drew up water from the mine bottom into both the valve chamber and the receiver and when the steam valve was re-opened the resulting pressure would close the suction valve **SV** and open the delivery valve **DV** to ensure that the water was discharged to a higher level via the delivery pipe **DP**. With water remaining in the system the condensing jet was operated once more and the cycle was repeated over and over again.

This was a simple system which did work and Captain *SAVERY* adopted a duplex arrangement of boilers and receivers in order that the operation of filling one of the receivers whilst the other one was being emptied was conducted simultaneously to maintain constant repetitive working. This twin receiver system was demonstrated by the inventor to the ROYAL SOCIETY in June 1699 being operated manually at that time; later on a mechanical method of opening the steam admission valves was introduced to enable one valve to be opened whilst the other one was closed and vice versa during the cycle. *SAVERY* described his invention in detail and in its final form in a book entitled "The Miner's Friend" which was published in 1701/1702.

For the practical draining of mines, *SAVERY*'s plan was to have the boilers and receivers erected at a height of about 20 feet above the bottom of the mine

gallery with the water discharge being effected at some 30 feet above the top of the receiver. At the point of discharge the suction rose of another set of *SAVERY* engines could be introduced and theoretically the water could then be raised to the next level and so on; whether or not this was actually done is open to conjecture. However, the system did have its problems for there was a great heat loss due to the alternate heating and cooling of the receiver which, combined with the limitations of the height of the raised water, only facilitated a short lift per unit. Another constraint on the *SAVERY* system was that the boilers of the day could only withstand a working pressure of 15 p.s.i. and, once again, this restricted water raising efficiency. *JOHN FAREY* in "A TREATISE on the STEAM ENGINE" (1827) demonstrated the layout of the SAVERY system in practice in Plate I of his work. Other illustrations of the system appeared in the Philosophical Transactions and in "The Miner's Friend".

In the early years of the 18th Century *THOMAS SAVERY* set up a workshop in Salisbury Court in London for the purpose of building his steam pumps and it is recorded that he supplied one to the order of a *Mr BALL* at Campden House in South Kensington: another was supplied to the York Buildings Waterworks but it did not appear to have been satisfactory. By 1705 the workshop was abandoned although perhaps some pumps for domestic houses may have been made. Some may have been supplied to Cornwall for mine drainage but it seems that the SAVERY machine was not suitable for this kind of work. Other personalities dabbled with the system, notably the Frenchman *DENIS PAPIN,* who made some improvements in 1707, and Dr. *J.T. DESAGULIERS* who published an account of an improved *SAVERY* engine in his "Experimental Philosophy" which was published between 1734 and 1744. Right up to the end of the 18th Century attempts were still being made to get the system improved with *WILLIAM BLAKEY* obtaining a patent as late as 1766 (Brit. Patent No. 848 of 10th June 1766) but with little better success. It appears that the final *SAVERY* unit to have been installed was a machine erected at the CITY GAS WORKS in London by *J. PONTIFEX* in 1822. (Fig. 1)

It is thought that by 1705 no further SAVERY pumps were installed in mines, for by this time the inventor was associated with *THOMAS NEWCOMEN;* however, after the discovery of water injection into a cylinder to cause a vacuum it has been stated that the SAVERY invention was improved by the use of a two-way valve between the boiler and the receiver and the placement of an internal rose in the latter to obviate the use of external coolant to condense the steam. However, *SAVERY's* use of condensed steam to cause a vacuum paved the way for *THOMAS NEWCOMEN* to perfect the 'Atmospheric' system and in turn produce the first steam pumping appliance using mechanical components to operate in the world. An interesting corollary of this story is that although the NEWCOMEN Engine revolutionised mine draining techniques, and rendered the SAVERY system obsolete for that purpose, *SAVERY's* ideas have persisted to the present day in the form of the "PULSOMETER" Pump, an efficient unit, having no proper mechanical parts to wear out except 'flap' valves working between two chambers.

THOMAS NEWCOMEN has been named as 'The father of the Industrial Revolution' for his work on the invention of the steam pumping engine which in turn became the base for all prime movers used throughout the industry down to the present day. His origins are shrouded in mystery and no portrait of him exists. He has been described variously as a blacksmith or an ironmonger and he was born in Dartmouth, living in a house in the town at Upper Street. He is believed to have been born in February 1663 and he died on 5th August 1729.

In 1705 *THOMAS NEWCOMEN* joined forces with

THOMAS SAVERY and another named *JOHN CALLEY* who has been described as a 'plumber'. Between them they set to work to make *NEWCOMEN's* vision a reality.

NEWCOMEN was not a 'man of science', but he was a practical engineer who had knowledge of the work that had preceded him, and the acumen to be able to combine the efforts of previous pioneers in order to perfect his invention. He utilised the piston and cylinder arrangement that had been experimented with by *DENIS PAPIN* and he must have been aware of the work of Sir *SAMUEL MORLAND* and the description in the diary of *ROGER NORTH* where steam from a separate boiler was used to act upon a piston or plunger in a closed cylinder. *MORLAND* and *NORTH* were contemporaries and in the State Papers of 1682 it was recorded that *MORLAND* had 'lately shown the King a plain proof of two several and distinct trials of a new invention for raising any quantity of water to any height by the help of fire alone'.

Whilst the NEWCOMEN engine worked very well, it was a crude and wasteful machine whose appetite for water and coals was legendary; there was, therefore, a great need for improvement and whilst men such as *JOHN SMEATON* tinkered with the original design in efforts to improve the machine's performance it was left to *JAMES WATT* to come up with ideas that were to transform the engine and to pave the way for the general use of steam power in industry. *WATT's* invention of the separate condenser and the use of steam on both sides of the piston had a two fold effect whereby heat was conserved and efficiency in the cylinder was nearly doubled. *WATT* also applied science to the art of engine building and he went on to develop the parallel motion linkage which did away with the arch-head chains, the cataract governor which adequately controlled the regulation of the power strokes and the use of cast iron beams in place of the wooden trussed units originally in vogue.

The outcome of the work done on pumping engines by *NEWCOMEN* and *WATT* was the perfection of the engine which worked on the *CORNISH* cycle. The CORNISH engine was developed for a variety of reasons, the most important of which was the lack of suitable fuel in Cornwall to cope with the prodigious appetite of the NEWCOMEN engine. The Cornish mine owners were dependent upon Wales for supplies of coal, and the costs of the fuel and its transport made the use of steam power somewhat prohibitive, for as well as those costs there was a levy of import duty which eventually

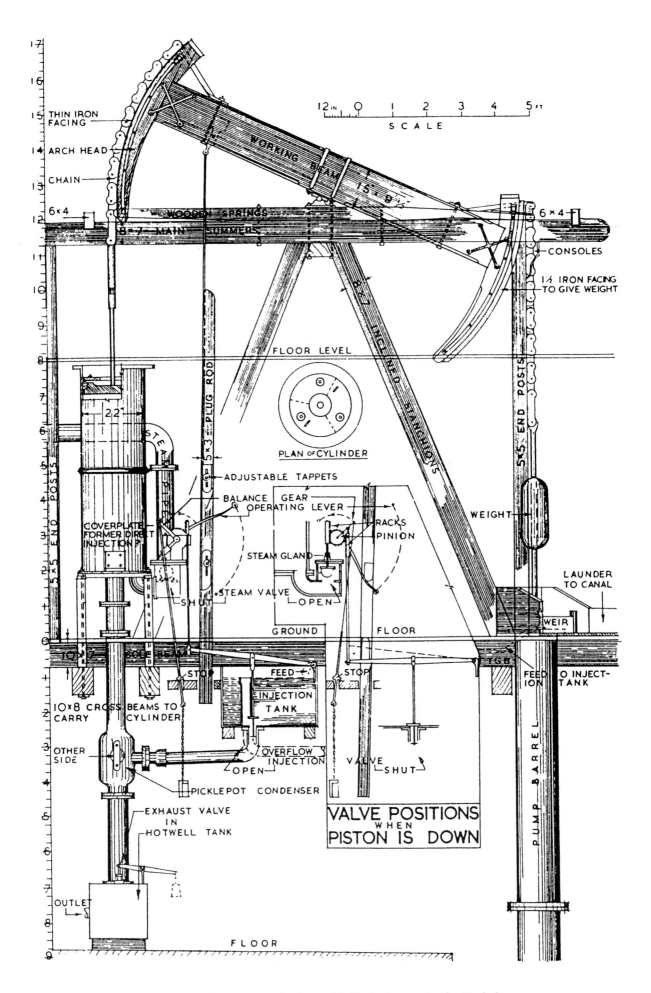

Fig. 2 - The 22" Newcomen Engine that stood beside the Coventry Canal at Hawkesbury.

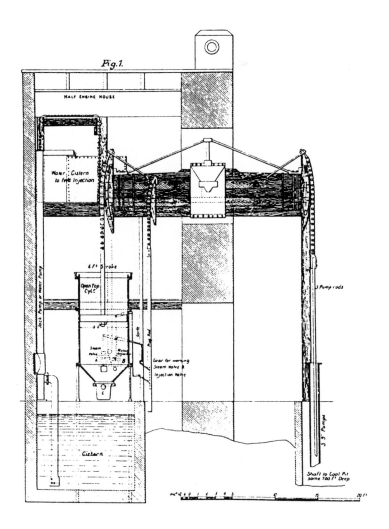
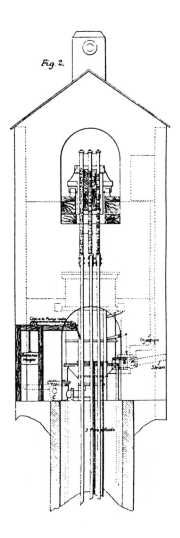

Fig. 3 -The South Liberty Colliery atmospheric engine.

reduced the number of NEWCOMEN engines at work in Cornwall to a single unit in 1740. However, by 1727, some fifteen years after the first NEWCOMEN engine had been erected, only five machines had been put to work in the county. The abolition of the import duty in the early 1740's gave a fillip to the industry and a number of engineers, notably *JOHN WISE, JOHN NANCARROW* and the *HORNBLOWER* family became active in Cornwall, being responsible for twenty or so engines by 1758. The rise to fame of the COALBROOKDALE COMPANY as a supplier of cast iron cylinders and other parts also assisted the fledgling industry to consolidate itself. By 1776 the first engine built by BOULTON & WATT was erected in Cornwall and the improvements to be found in their power unit soon rendered the NEWCOMEN type obsolete in Cornwall and obsolescent elsewhere.

Although great savings in fuel were made by the introduction of the WATT engine in Cornwall with one company, *GREAT CONSOLS*, saving £9,000 per annum, eventually there was a problem with the royalties extracted from the mine owners by *BOULTON & WATT*; while in times of prosperity the mine owners were happy to remunerate the engine builders this was not the case when trade slackened off. The mine owners became very angry at what they saw as an excessive levy and soon   challenges were made to WATT's patent of 1769 and many efforts were made to circumvent it. *JONATHAN HORNBLOWER* was the first engineer to challenge *BOULTON & WATT* by taking out a patent in 1781 for a twin cylinder engine, and despite a 'war of words', no recourse to law was made by the Birmingham firm. However, in the case of *EDWARD BULL*, who was an easier nut to crack, *BOULTON & WATT* proceeded with litigation in 1793 and gained an injunction in the following year on the grounds that *BULL's* engine was a 'manifest piracy'. For 25 years *BOULTON & WATT* had exerted a stranglehold on the Duchy with the levying of royalties and by threatening injunctions on engine builders and mine owners alike. By attacking the

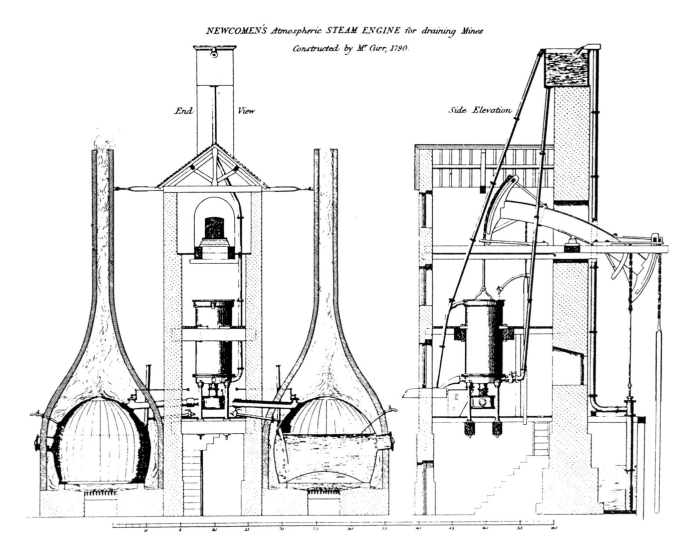

NEWCOMEN'S Atmospheric STEAM ENGINE for draining Mines

Constructed by M.ͬ Curr, 1790.

End View

Side Elevation

Fig. 4 -The 61" Newcomen Engine erected at Attercliffe Common Colliery by John Curr of Sheffield in 1790.

mine owners *BOULTON & WATT* avoided any challenge to the validity of their patent, as would have been the case if they went for the engine builders and this was, therefore, a safer option. Eventually they had to uphold their patent and this was done in an action against *JABEZ CARTER*, a member of the *HORNBLOWER* family, whereby the validity of the patent was confirmed in 1799. This was really a hollow victory for *BOULTON & WATT* for in the following year their patent expired and the Cornishmen were then allowed to go their own way.

The year of 1800, the dawn of a new and exciting century from an engineering standpoint, was crucial to the development of the steam pumping engine for with the withdrawal of *BOULTON & WATT* from Cornwall upon the expiry of their patent, the local men began to improve engines to suit their needs. One of the first of these men was *JOEL LEAN*, a mine

engineer and manager, who, together with *TREVITHICK* and *MURDOCH*, was involved in such improvements. In 1801, for example, *LEAN* changed the pumps from bucket to plunger lift and improved the water raising efficiency; he was followed by others such as *ARTHUR WOOLF*, *WILLIAM SIMS*, *JOHN HOCKING* and *MICHAEL LOAM*. All of these engineers and many more contributed to the on-going success of the CORNISH Engine enabling it to be constructed in the sizes as big as 100" cylinder diameter, with the largest being 144" diameter engines for Holland. Three large foundries operated in Cornwall during the 19th Century and these supplied the needs of the county as well as having extensive trade in other parts of the country and abroad; they were the COPPERHOUSE FOUNDRY, (set up by the CORNISH COPPER Co. and later owned by SANDYS, VIVIAN & Co.) of Hayle, HARVEY & Co. also of Hayle and the PERRAN FOUNDRY later known as FOXES &

PERRAN FOUNDRY Co. and finally as WILLIAMS' PERRAN FOUNDRY Co. These, together with many smaller facilities such as the TAMAR IRONWORKS, the ROSELAND VALE FOUNDRY and the WADEBRIDGE FOUNDRY, made the County of Cornwall self sufficient for engines and engineering supplies; anything from a small screw to a mighty 100" engine could be had in Cornwall. The last Cornish Engine to be constructed was made by HARVEY & Co in 1899 for the HODBARROW MINING Co. of Millom in Cumbria, whilst the last to operate in service was the SEVERN TUNNEL engine which was shut down in 1962.

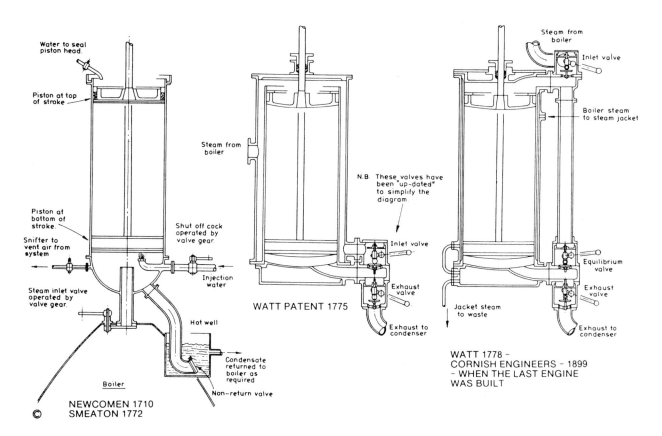

Diagram B - The Newcomen, the Watt and the Cornish systems compared.

Reproduced by courtsey of R. Simmons Esq.

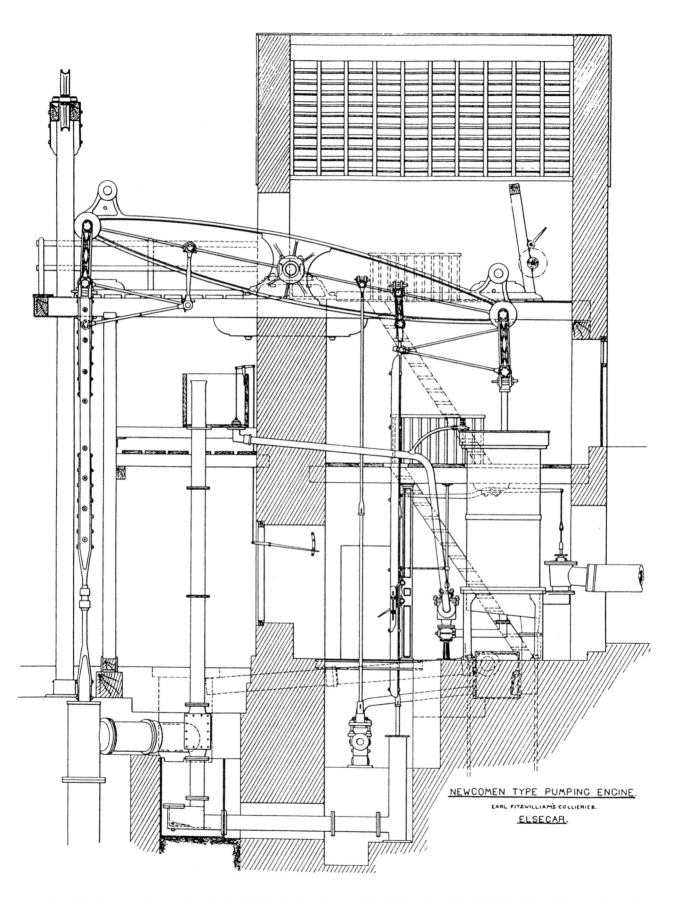

NEWCOMEN TYPE PUMPING ENGINE.
EARL FITZWILLIAM'S COLLIERIES.
ELSECAR.

Fig. 5: The Newcomen atmospheric engine that is believed to have been erected in 1787 and worked until 1918 at Elsecar. It was used again in 1928 when the electric pumps that superseded it were flooded, and it remained in an operable state as a stand-by until the end of World War II. It is now preserved.

Chapter 2: The Newcomen Engine

It has been noted that the SAVERY apparatus was capable of being useful to a certain extent for the purpose of raising water but, due to its limited lift, it was not an effective proposition for the mine owner. With the advent of the proposals by *THOMAS NEWCOMEN* and his partners in 1705 there was, indeed, hope that the need to clear deep workings of flood water would soon be realised. Early experimentations with the introduction of steam beneath a piston inside a cylinder, and the condensation of that steam by means of the application of cold water to the exterior of the cylinder, did prove that the pressure of the atmosphere alone could force the piston to the base of the cylinder. Having discovered that this principle worked it was soon decided to put it into practice by building a full sized engine to demonstrate its operation properly. Consequently, the partners went on to construct the first machine and this was a reality by 1712. Accounts concerning the venue of this engine vary, with some authorities stating that it was erected 'near Wolverhampton', and others saying that it was at Dudley Castle in the County of Staffordshire. There is definite proof for the latter location as documentary evidence and an illustration in the form of an engraving still exist.

After struggling for some time to make the engine work continuously *NEWCOMEN* was surprised "to see the engine go several strokes, and very quick together, when, after a search he found a hole in the piston which let the cold water in to condense the steam in the inside of the cylinder, whereas before it had always been done on the outside". This was the turning point in the effectiveness of the invention for it rendered the exterior cold water jacket unnecessary. From thereon *NEWCOMEN* manufactured his engines in accordance with the design shown in DIAGRAM 'C' where all of the elements which comprise the 'Atmospheric Engine' are illustrated in sectional form.

THOMAS NEWCOMEN had put in about fourteen years of development work before he achieved the success that was rightly due to him when the Dudley Castle machine was erected in 1712. Some details concerning this engine are interesting for it was quite a small affair when compared to later units; it had a cylinder diameter of 21 ins. and it stood at a height of 7 ft. 10 ins. Its performance was satisfactory for it could operate continuously at 12 strokes per

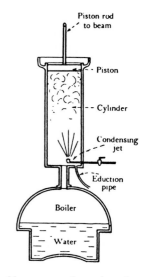

Newcomen engine - schematic layout of operation.

minute to lift 10 Imp. gallons of water from a depth of 153 feet at each stroke to discharge to a drainage adit linked to the main shaft. Other engines soon followed the 1712 unit and machines are known to have been erected at Whitehaven and Hawarden as early as 1715 and 1716 respectively. However, some problems ensued during this period, for another engine supplied to Moor Hall Colliery, near Leeds, at about the same time did not seem to have been as successful as the previous three and, apparently, only lasted for some four years. In construction the Moor Hall engine was similar to the others having a cylinder dimension of 23 ins. and a stroke of 72 ins. and being credited with a lift of 111 ft. to adit at 12 strokes per minute when working automatically, being increased to 15 strokes when controlled manually. *NEWCOMEN* spent a considerable amount of time repairing the Leeds engine and his partner, *JOHN CALLEY*, is reputed to have died nearby at Austhorpe in 1717 whilst engaged upon these repairs. There has been some dispute about the death of *CALLEY* at this time for there is a record of a *JOHN CALLEY* dying in March 1725 in Holland who was also an associate of *NEWCOMEN*. The probable explanation for this is that the *JOHN CALLEY* who died in the Leeds area was the original partner, whilst the other death was that of either his son or nephew.

After these beginnings, with the success of the NEWCOMEN engine being more or less assured, the apparatus soon became popular with mine owners and others and although the cost of them at about £1,200 was astronomical at the time, there was an obvious need for such equipment and customers were willing to pay the price. The first engine for waterworks use was the unit constructed for the YORK BUILDINGS WATERWORKS by the Strand in London which was erected in 1762; this engine did attract some unwelcome publicity at the time for Londoners objected to smoke pollution from it. This factor had not arisen before as the engines were usually supplied to mining areas where smoke and other pollutants were taken for granted in the 1700s. Very soon an export market was established for the NEWCOMEN engine on the Continent, firstly with an engine being sent out to the city of Konigsberg in Hungary to be followed with other examples supplied to what is now the Czech Republic, and then to Belgium, Austria, Sweden, Spain and France. The Swedish engine was originally mooted by Colonel *JOHN O'KELLY*, who possibly may have been an ancestor of the writer, but his role in the proceedings has always been reported as being 'elusive'. The first NEWCOMEN engine to be built for the U.S.A. was erected at the ARLINGTON COPPER WORKS in the State of Maine between 1753 and 1755; this work was overseen by a member of the *HORNBLOWER* family, *JOSIAH*, and its cylinder still survives in the National Collection at the SMITHSONIAN INSTITUTION.

Operation and Technical Details of the NEWCOMEN Engine

The operation of the NEWCOMEN engine and its technical details make interesting reading in the light of modern technology, for at the time of its inception and early usage many difficulties in the construction of the component parts, the correct methods of erection and in the adjustments for continuous running appeared. As with all new technology an industry devoted to the building of the engines soon came into being, and many engineers appeared to take advantage of the invention.

Referring to DIAGRAM 'C', the NEWCOMEN Engine consisted of a boiler surmounted by the piston and cylinder, with the piston rod being connected to a heavy wooden beam which rocked on trunnion bearings situated on a specially strengthened outer wall of the engine house; at each end of the beam were two 'arch-heads' to which there were fixed link chains. On each power stroke, atmospheric pressure forced the piston down to pull on the 'in-house' chain which in turn rocked the beam to lift the pump-rods attached to the 'out-of-house' chain; when the power stroke was spent the weight of the pump-rods rocked the beam 'out-of-

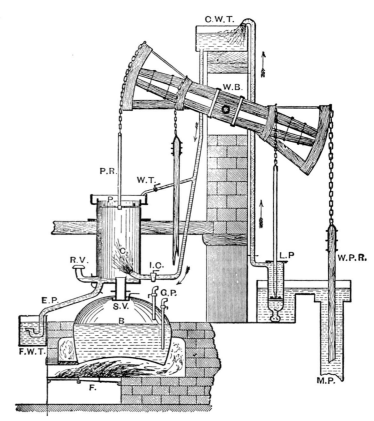

NEWCOMEN'S ATMOSPHERIC ENGINE, 1712.

F	for	Furnace.		M P	for	Mine pump.
B	,,	Boiler.		L P	,,	Lift pump.
G P	,,	Gauge pipes.		C W T	,,	Cold-water tank.
S V	,,	Steam valve.		W T	,,	Water tap to top of piston
C	,,	Cylinder.		I C	,,	Injection cock.
P	,,	Piston.		R V	,,	Relief or snifting valve.
P R	,,	Piston rod.		E P	,,	Eduction pipe.
W B	,,	Wooden beam.		F W T	,,	Feed-water tank.
W P R	,,	Weighted pump rod.				

Diagram C - Newcomen's 1712 atmospheric engine - operation.

house' and carried the piston to the top of the cylinder again and then the cycle was repeated.

Referring to the drawing, the method of operation in detail was as follows: the Furnace **F** fired a 'haystack' boiler B to produce steam at a pressure of about 5 p.s.i. which flooded into the cylinder when the piston was at the top of its stroke and the steam valve **SV** opened. When the cylinder was filled with steam, the valve **SV** was closed and the water injection cock **IC** was opened; this water condensed the stream in the cylinder to cause a vacuum to be formed beneath the piston, which was then driven downwards by the pressure of the atmosphere (14.7 p.s.i.) to bring the beam 'in-house' and, hence, lift the pump rods which were connected to a pump bucket at the base of the mine. When the piston had reached the bottom of its stroke any residual water left in the cylinder was driven out via the eduction pipe **EP** to a separate feed-water tank, and any air in the system was released through the 'snifter' or relief valve **RV**. This latter valve was so named by *NEWCOMEN* because of the curious noise that it made. By now the weight of the pump rods etc. was sufficient to draw the piston to the top of the cylinder, and the beam was said to be 'out-of-house'. Other apparatus shown in the drawing included the lift pump, **LP**, to feed the cold water tank for injection and also to provide a water seal on the top of the piston to prevent steam and vacuum losses. Ancillary chain drives to operate the lift pump and a feed water pump were placed in-board of the arch-heads and these were called 'little arches'. At first all of the valves and cocks were operated manually and the engine man had to go around opening and shutting them; firstly he would ensure that the water seal on top of the piston was made, then he would open the steam valve. When the beam came 'in-house' after the steam valve had been shut, and the injection valve opened, that injection valve would be shut and the eduction valve opened to release the residual water. He also had to operate the try cocks on the gauge pipes on the boiler to ensure that water levels were maintained inside the vessel. All of this was very labour intensive and arduous and soon after its inception the *NEWCOMEN* engine was fitted with automatic valve gear. The move towards automation came unexpectedly, so the story goes. The popular theory is that an attendant, a boy name *POTTER*, tiring of the monotonous task of operating all of the valves, connected them together in sequence with lines of cord. In the manual form of operation the attendant had to be very wary in case the piston hit the base of the cylinder, or allowed the piston to be drawn out of the cylinder at the top of the stroke, allowing the beam to go 'out-of-house' with disastrous results; with automatic operation, stops were fitted to prevent either of the above mishaps and strong cords were fitted to operate the valves. These cords etc. were gradually replaced with rods, catches and detents and in 1718 a Land Surveyor and engineer named *BEIGHTON* is thought to have formulated a co-ordinated form of

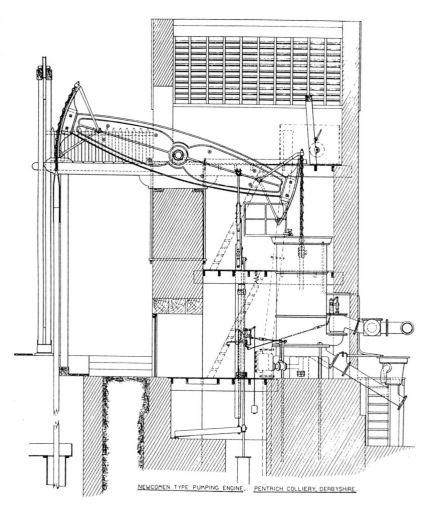

Fig. 6 - The Newcomen atmospheric engine built by Francis Thompson for Oakerthorpe Colliery in 1791. It was removed to Pentrich Colliery in 1841 and worked, in total, for a period of 127 years.

valve gear when he erected a NEWCOMEN Engine at Oxclose. Incorporated with the valve gear was another piece of equipment called the 'buoy' which ensured that another power stroke was not made until the boiler had recovered sufficiently to enable it to provide enough steam for the following cycle. Unfortunately over a space of nearly three hundred years the stories of invention and modification and their creators have become muddled; some credit *HENRY BEIGHTON* with the valve gear improvements, whilst other give the sole credit to *NEWCOMEN* and *CALLEY*; the boy *POTTER* has always been credited with the invention of the 'Scoggan', or detent, but this is open to discussion. Some details of the method of the operation of the valve gear are shown in the diagrams on the next page which shows the steam admission gear and the injection valve gear. With the atmospheric engine *NEWCOMEN* managed to hold a pressure of 6.4 p.s.i. continuously in the cylinder – no mean feat at the time.

Early Valve-gear Systems used on NEWCOMEN Engines

The Steam Admission Valve:

When NEWCOMEN engines were originally fitted with the means for working automatically, the arrangements were constructed according to the drawings depicted on the right. For the admission of steam, the valve at **A** oscillated from side to side to close or uncover a port in the pipe from the boiler to the cylinder; this was actuated as follows: As the Plug Rod **O** rose and fell, a pin moved the little 'Y' lever **M** up and down to rock the arbour **G** which in turn imparted a motion to the 'Y' Lever **H** which had a weight at its extremity to enable it to go over centre. This allowed the stirrup **E** to move horizontally and pull the 'spanner' up against one of the stops at **C**. The 'spanner' was attached to a spindle which in turn was fixed to the admission valve. This system allowed the position of the beam to determine the admission of steam.

The Injection Valve:

This system also worked on the plug rod at **M** and, as it descended, it depressed the end of the 'F' Lever **C** until it reached the closed position where it was retained by the detent **H**. At this point the 'buoy' took over, for the steam valve having opened and filled the cylinder as the engine went 'out-of-house', the buoy precluded another power stroke until the boiler had recovered. When the steam dome on the boiler became re-filled, the pressure inside allowed the buoy to rise and release the detent rod and allow the 'F' Lever to fall by gravity and so open the injection cock. The 'POTTER CORD' allowed manual over-ride as well as controlling the detent.

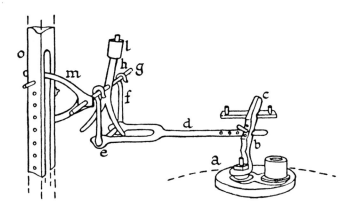

A.	Valve spindle	F.	Stirrup hangers
B.	Valve spanner	G.	Arbor
C.	Spanner stops	H.	"Y" lever
D.	Horizontal link	L.	Tumbling bob
E.	Stirrup	M.	Little "Y" lever
		O.	Plug rod

Steam admission valve gear.

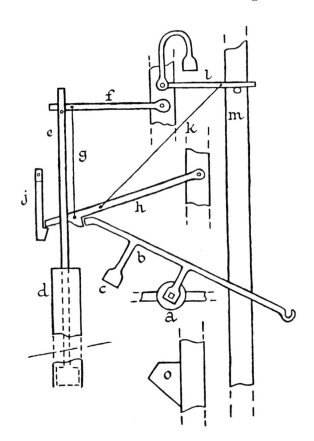

A.	Injection cock	G.	Buoy tappet to detent cord
B.	"F" lever	H.	Detent or "Scoggan"
C.	"F" lever weight	J.	Detent stop
D.	Buoy and buoy pipe	K.	"Potter cord" to detent
E.	Buoy rod	L.	"Potter cord" tappet
F.	Buoy rod tappet	M.	Plug rod
		O.	"F" lever stop

Injection valve gear.

Drawing From "The Steam Engine of Thomas Newcomen" reproduced courtesy of Landmark Publishing.

Subsequent Historical Data concerning the NEWCOMEN Engine.

Following the death of THOMAS SAVERY on the 15th May in 1715, his patent rights were passed on to his wife, MARTHA, who by the good offices of JOHN MERES, the Secretary of the Worshipful Company of Apothecaries, was able to have them invested in a Joint-Stock Company which was known by the title of "The Proprietors of the Invention for Raising Water by the Impellant Force of Fire". The governing body of this organisation was known as the "Committee of the Proprietors" and amongst others, THOMAS NEWCOMEN was an important member; most of the other personalities involved in this committee had influence in the City of London. These Proprietors sought to contain the Patent and licence its use to selected engineers and engine builders and thus preserve a monopoly; to this end an advertisement appeared in the LONDON GAZETTE for the 11th/14th of August 1716 which gave notice that 'any person desirous to treat with the Proprietors for such engines' should repair to a coffee-house in Birchin Lane to see one of the Proprietors, EDWARD ELLIOT, every Wednesday to discuss terms.

Of course this monopoly exerted a stranglehold on the industry in the same way that BOULTON & WATT managed to do later on in the 18th Century and H. J. LAWSON and GEORGE B. SELDEN did to the motor industry at the end of the 19h Century. However, as the Patent expired in 1733, the power of the Proprietors was curtailed as the invention came into the public domain and the payment of royalties ceased. Nevertheless the Proprietors did have a good run for their money, for in the period between 1712 and 1733, some 110 engines had been erected at home and overseas and the NEWCOMEN system became an established form of effective motive power.

Improvements to the NEWCOMEN Engine:

It has been noted previously that although the NEWCOMEN engine was, indeed, 'fit for purpose' it was inefficient in the use of fuel and water and, therefore, there was a great need for improvement. Notwithstanding that the invention was the 'wonder of the age' and that its appearance in the 18th Century was akin to the Moon Landings in 1969 during the 20th Century, there was, as with the Moon Project, a hiatus following the lapse of the SAVERY Patent during which little or nothing was achieved by way of advancement.

One of the main problems that had to be overcome was the restriction on cylinder diameter occasioned by the use of brass for the castings. In the early days of the NEWCOMEN engine, brass could be machined more accurately than other materials but it restricted the size to diameters below 36 ins. This persisted to the 1720s until ABRAHAM DARBY perfected the casting of engine cylinders in iron at his COALBROOKDALE IRON WORKS. For a period of forty years the COALBROOKDALE concern enjoyed their own monopoly of cylinder casting and by 1761 they were able to produce cylinders as big as 74½ ins. diameter by 120 ins. in length. The demand for these iron cylinders started slowly but it soon accelerated and, with the appearance of the BOULTON & WATT engine in the 1770s and 1780s, the demand for larger cylinders weighing over 6 tons each outstripped the resources of the COALBROOKDALE firm.

It was left to JOHN SMEATON, the builder of the Eddystone Lighthouse, to effect real and lasting improvements to the NEWCOMEN engine. Whereas earlier engineers had tended to work empirically, SMEATON introduced an element of science into his modifications. The methods of empirical working did stultify improvement and SMEATON's work enhanced the performance of the atmospheric engine. JOHN SMEATON formulated a system of measurement of the performance of engines which he called the 'duty' – this measurement was the amount of water in millions of pounds (a.v.d.) that could be raised one foot high per bushel of coal (a bushel weighing 84 lbs.). This standard enabled one engine to be compared to another to ascertain relative efficiency. He selected some NEWCOMEN engines at work on Tyneside for comparison and he found that loadings and overall performance varied greatly – a well loaded engine from point of view of piston pressure did not necessarily point to the best duty achieved and he found in his studies that a 60 ins. machine performed better than one having a cylinder diameter of 75 ins.! The former engine achieved some 3 h.p. better than the latter when translated into horse-power figures. The reason for this discrepancy lay in the degree of accuracy of manufacture of the components, and SMEATON discovered that some of the cylinders allowed the piston to be slack in the bore, whilst others were tight; valve gear did not admit the right quantity of steam to work effectively and so on. Other factors were present such as too short a stroke, boiler grates pitched too low to provide the correct heat values to be extracted from the fuel whilst too much water accumulated on top of the piston to cause excessive cooling. *SMEATON* was associated with another famous ironworks of the time which was the first such enterprise in Scotland – the CARRON IRONWORKS – noted for their 'pot-bellied' coke stoves today. This foundry went into production in 1760 and *SMEATON* designed the plant there; one of the tools that he introduced was an accurate cylinder boring mill which could produce a truly circular bore. The entrance of the CARRON IRONWORKS into the fray ended the COALBROOKDALE monopoly.

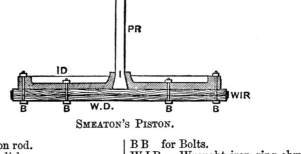

SMEATON'S PISTON.

PR for Piston rod.
ID „ Iron dish.
WD „ Wooden dish.

BB for Bolts.
WIR „ Wrought iron ring shrunk on like a cart-wheel tyre.

Diagram D.

Amongst the improvements that *SMEATON* effected were his special form of piston, shown in Diagram 'D', an improvement on the NEWCOMEN type which had consisted of a flat plate with a broad strip of leather screwed to it and turned up at the sides some two or three inches in the cylinder. This piston gave considerable trouble owing to its irregular fit which caused leakage and the fact that the leather was often cut up being then worse than useless. *SMEATON* applied scientific data to the admission of steam and the amount of injection water needed to cause condensation in the cylinder with the wooden underside of his piston preventing waste in this direction. He introduced a feed-water heater system and increased the flexibility of the working strokes by means of regulation of steam volumes rather than shortening the stroke and replacing the 'buoy' system with a 'cataract' which allowed a water trough and cup system to vary the weight operating the 'F' Lever which controlled the injection cock. When the engine worked at maximum power the cataract was put out of use, but as loads decreased due to there being less water in the mine, the cataract could be linked to the cycle to regulate the number of strokes per minute by adjusting the amount of water held in the cup to achieve a variable weight effect. *SMEATON* adopted a hemispherical cylinder bottom and a laminated timber beam with its trunnions set at its mid-point instead of below as had been the norm when timber baulk beams were used.

All of *SMEATON's* improvements were embodied in his 52 ins. engine erected at the LONG BENTON COLLIERY, Northumberland in 1722 (Fig. 7). This engine worked at 12½ strokes per minute on a mean effective pressure of 7.5 p.s.i. to return a duty of 9.45 millions, whereas the best recorded duty figure that he had found on Tyneside was only 7.44 millions. *SMEATON* then built a number of other engines that included his improvements and these were located at Chacewater in Cornwall where he built a 72 ins. machine in 1775, at Kronstadt in Imperial Russia where a 66 ins. engine was supplied for emptying docks, and several others that were used variously in mines and waterworks.

Another improver of the atmospheric engine was one *JOHN CURR* of Sheffield who decided to locate the boilers remotely to obviate the need to mount the cylinder over the boiler steam-dome. JOHN CURR wrote a book entitled "The Coal Viewer & Engine-Builder's Companion" which was published in 1797 and following this he erected a 61 ins. engine at Attercliffe Common Colliery in 1790, (Fig. 4), which embodied his principles. For this plant he used two boilers located in outhouses alongside the engine-house and these were connected together by means of a common steam pipe which joined in a chest beneath the cylinder; this configuration enabled *CURR* to build a more compact engine house which provided a greater degree of support for the cylinder and its ancillary equipment. Previously, when the cylinder was mounted atop the boiler, there were fractures in steam pipes and failures in the jointing because the cylinder, not being adequately supported, tended to flex excessively at each stroke and cause such problems. Another improvement made by *CURR* was to increase the elevation of the injection water cistern, placing it on an extended wall of the house to be situated well above the roof. The stroke of the Attercliffe Common Colliery engine was 8½ ft. and it made 12 strokes per minute to return a duty of 9.38 millions.

Other modifications to the original NEWCOMEN style of engine are noteworthy and they include the introduction of the 'pickle-pot' condenser, the replacement of the link chain by the pitch-chain (like a bicycle chain with plates and rollers) on the arch-heads and the fitment of drop-valves and sliding-valves in place of the plug cocks. The 'pickle-pot' condenser was placed below the cylinder and it was in direct communication with it through a large diameter pipe; cold water was injected into the 'pickle-pot' instead of into the cylinder and later on in the cycle the incoming steam blew the condensate and any air present out via a non-return valve that was loaded at about 2 p.s.i. This method was not too efficient though it did possess the advantage that

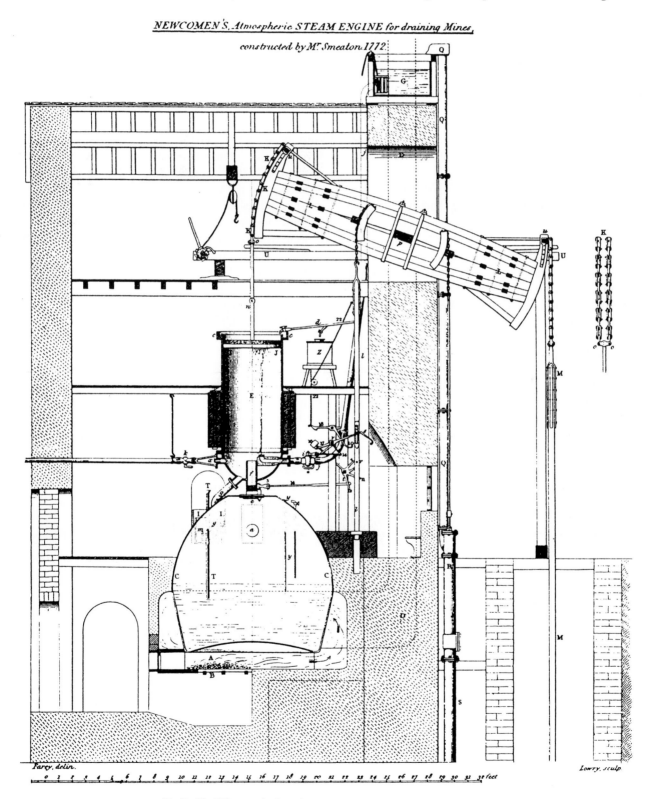

Fig. 7 - The 52" atmospheric engine at Long Benton Colliery in Northumberland which embodied the improvements made by John Smeaton in 1772.

when the steam was admitted into the cylinder it was not exposed to so great a volume of condensate as hitherto. Messrs. *BOULTON & WATT* always considered the 'pickle-pot' condenser to be an infringement of their 1769 Patent, though they are never recorded as having resorted to litigation to suppress its use. However, many features of the improved engine as built by *BOULTON & WATT* were incorporated in atmospheric engines erected after the lapse of the 1769 Patent in 1800, and these included the use of the separate condenser, the fitting of the *WATT* water cataract governor together with drop and sliding valves and the replacement of the wooden beams with cast-iron units having the *WATT* parallel motion at the piston rod end.

Notes on Important NEWCOMEN Engines and those Existing Today

One of the most famous NEWCOMEN Engines to be documented was that erected at the South Liberty Colliery which was owned by the ASHTON VALE IRONWORKS of Bedminster in Bristol. This engine, which is depicted in Fig. 3, was the last atmospheric unit to operate in the West of England and it was one of the longest lived, working from about 1750 until 1900 when, unfortunately, it was scrapped. Luckily it was extensively documented by *BRYAN DONKIN M.I.C.E.* in the journal "ENGINEERING" for their issue of the 25th October 1895. In the article, which was derived from fieldwork carried out by *H.W. PEARSON M.Inst. Mech. E.* in the May of that year, there were several supporting photographs of the old engine together with drawings (Fig. 3) and, interestingly, an Indicator diagram.

The South Liberty Engine was seen in the photographs to have retained its massive, wooden, laminated beam made on the SMEATON pattern and which measured 24 ft ins length by about 4 ft. in depth as well as having pitch-chains on the arch-heads instead of link-chains; the cylinder dimension was 66 ins. and it had a stroke of 6 ft. This cylinder was designed with a conical bottom to gain ease of condensate drainage in a similar manner to SMEATON's hemispherical shape, and it weighed 6 tons. The Indicator Diagram, alluded to previously, recorded a boiler pressure of 2.3 p.s.i. and a mean effective pressure of 9.5 p.s.i. at a rate of 10 strokes per minute – this gave a Horse Power rating of 52.72. When one considers the weight of the engine in total, the boiler, the pitwork and the pumps, the horse power per ton figure is minimal, but nevertheless, these engines did do their work well considering the time at which they were made. Over

its 150 years of use, the South Liberty Engine worked for about 5 hours per day, for 6 days a week. The engine-man who was driving it in 1895 had driven it since he was a boy, his father and grand-father having driven it before him.

Another important machine was the 72 ins. Chacewater engine erected by *JOHN SMEATON* in 1775 which has been mentioned previously. It was one of the most powerful NEWCOMEN prime movers that had been made up to that time and it was the largest such engine to work in Cornwall – with a stroke of 9 ft. and going at 9 strokes per minute it developed 76 h.p. It was fitted with SMEATON's laminated wooden beam which measured 27 ft. 4 ins. in length, by 2 ft. wide and 6 ft. 2 ins. deep at its centre; this beam was made up from twenty pieces of fir measuring 12 ins. x 6 ins. in section and all bolted together. The Chacewater engine worked three 16¼ ins. pumps in series which drew water from a depth of 306 ft. to adit level. Apparently it did not last long as an atmospheric engine for in 1778 it was re-built by *JAMES WATT* being fitted with a new 63 ins. cylinder which was cast by *WILKINSON*; the original cylinder was retained and was used as an outer casing for the new one.

From research that was conducted during the latter half of the 20th Century, it appears that 1454 NEWCOMEN or atmospheric engines were constructed world-wide by the end of the 18th Century just prior to the expiry of the BOULTON & WATT Patent in 1800. If one counts the two rotative units that are preserved in Scotland and in the U.S.A., only seven survive to the present day. The following is a list, with descriptions, of the five non-rotative NEWCOMEN Engines in preservation:

(1) FAIRBOTTOM VALLEY

This engine was situated at Bardsley near Ashton-under Lyne. It has a cylinder dimension of 28 ins. and it was built in circa. 1760. It worked for 70 years, being stopped in 1830. It was used to pump out the Cannel Mine and after 1830 it lay derelict for one hundred years, gradually mouldering away. However, in 1930 it was acquired by the automobile magnate, *HENRY FORD*, who restored it and re-erected it at the HENRY FORD MUSEUM in Dearborn, Michigan, U.S.A. where it remains today. It does not have its original boiler with it but has a 'haystack' boiler that is representative of its period. It rejoiced in the name of 'Fairbottom Bobs' in its heyday.

(2) WINDMILL END

This engine was installed by the Staffordshire Mines Drainage Commissioners at the Windmill End Pumping Station and is a non-rotative pumping engine. It is also at the HENRY FORD MUSEUM in Dearborn.

(3) PENTRICH

This engine was built by *FRANCIS THOMSON* in 1791 and erected at Oakerthorpe Colliery. It was removed to Pentrich Colliery in 1841 and, altogether, had a working life of 127 years. It is depicted in Fig. 6 and it is now located in the Motive Power Gallery of the NATIONAL MUSEUM of SCIENCE & INDUSTRY at South Kensington in London. It was dismantled in the 1920s and re-erected in London using materials taken from the old engine house at Pentrich. Originally the engine had a wooden beam but when it was moved to Pentrich a cast-iron beam was fitted.

(4) ELSECAR

This engine was built in 1795 and is the only NEWCOMEN Engine to remain on the site where it was installed. This engine worked until 1923 when it was superseded by electric pumps. The electric pumps failed during 1928 due to flooding and the NEWCOMEN engine had to be brought back into use for a few weeks until the electric units were repaired. It remained on standby until the early 1950s by which time it was owned by the NATIONAL COAL BOARD. Today it is preserved and open to the General Public. (Fig. 5)

(5) HAWKESBURY JUNCTION

This engine was purchased by the COVENTRY CANAL Co. from a gentleman named JONATHAN WOODHOUSE in 1821 but its original date of manufacture is not known. Although it is of an early pattern it probably dates from the late 18th Century. It has a simple wooden beam, is fitted with a 'pickle-pot' condenser and has a cylinder dimension of 22 ins. Its use was to pump water from a well into the

Coventry Canal and it did this until 1913; it then lay unused and undisturbed for 50 years when the BRITISH TRANSPORT COMMISSION donated it to the NEWCOMEN SOCIETY for the Study of History of Engineering & Technology. This engine was moved and re-erected at Dartmouth in 1963 by a member of the Society, *ARTHUR PYNE*, and was named as the "NEWCOMEN Memorial Engine". On the 17th of September 1981 the engine was designated as an International Historic Mechanical Engineering Landmark under the auspices of the AMERICAN SOCIETY of MECHANICAL ENGINEERS, the NEWCOMEN SOCIETY and the INSTITUTION of MECHANICAL ENGINEERS. It was the 67th designation since the Historical Recognition Programme was instituted in 1973 and the third outside of the United States of America. The machine is open to the General Public at the NEWCOMEN ENGINE HOUSE & DARTMOUTH MUSEUM on the Butterwalk at Dartmouth in Devon, the birthplace of *THOMAS NEWCOMEN*. The drawing in Fig. 2 was made by the late *Dr. C.T.G. BOUCHER*.

Other items of interest concerning NEWCOMEN ENGINES may be seen at the SCIENCE MUSEUM in London where, in addition to the Pentrich Engine, there is a model of SMEATON's Long Benton Colliery Engine made to a scale of 1:12 which is located in the Motive Power Gallery on the Ground Floor. At the same venue there is a piston and rod cap and the arch-head chains from the Newmarket Silkstone Colliery engine "Old Sarah" (also in the Motive Power Gallery), a part section model in 1:12 scale of a NEWCOMEN mine pumping engine in the "Synopsis Gallery" and another working model of a NEWCOMEN engine in store. There is a model to 1/3rd scale of a NEWCOMEN Engine in the GREATER MANCHESTER MUSEUM of SCIENCE & INDUSTRY and a full-sized working replica of the 1712 NEWCOMEN Engine is to be found at the BLACK COUNTRY MUSEUM at Dudley in the West Midlands. The ROYAL SCOTTISH MUSEUM in Edinburgh has the 1820 Farme Colliery rotative NEWCOMEN winding engine. Besides this there is a part of a piston from the Arlington engine in the SMITHSONIAN INSTITUTE in the U.S.A.

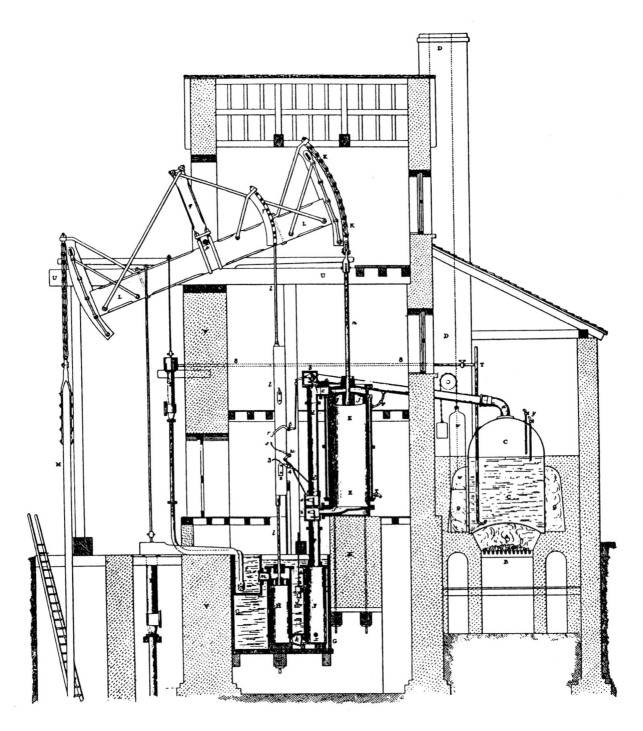

Fig. 8 - Boulton & Watt Pumping Engine of 1798.

CHAPTER 3: THE BOULTON & WATT ENGINE

During the first half of the 18th Century with only *SAVERY, NEWCOMEN* and the "Proprietors" operating in the field, there did not seem to be a need for the extensive patenting of ideas relating to the 'Fire Engine'; so much so, that *THOMAS NEWCOMEN* decided to develop his engine under the protection of the SAVERY umbrella rather than attempting circumvention. However, although the SAVERY Patent appeared to be all embracing at the time there must have been 'a chink in the armour' for one *MARTEN TRIEWALD*, who also erected the first NEWCOMEN engine in Sweden at Dannemora Mine in 1727, had previously applied for, and

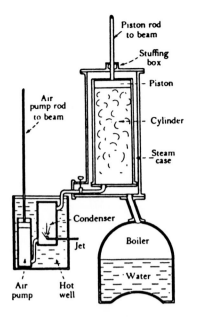

Boulton & Watt engine - schematic layout of operation.

had been granted, Letters Patent at the British Patent Office in 1722. The specification of this patent, (Brit. Pat. No 449 of the 29th June 1722), was entitled as a "Machine for Drawing Water out of Mines & Collieries by the Power of the Atmosphere".

This could only have been a description of a NEWCOMEN style of engine and it is interesting to consider how it managed to avoid clashing with the SAVERY invention. Nevertheless, whilst "The Proprietors" managed to reap a good harvest there appears to be no record of *TRIEWALD* extracting royalties for his specification.

In the second half of the 18th Century patents came very quickly as inventors sought recognition of their ideas. Many well-known names applied for protection during this period and the most famous of these was *JAMES WATT* who was granted his groundbreaking patent for the 'Separate Condenser' on the 5th January 1769, (Brit. Pat. No. 913 of 1769). The protection afforded by this patent enabled *WATT* in collaboration with *MATTHEW BOULTON*, who was a financier and manufacturer, to exert a very tight rein on the whole of the steam engine industry until 1800. It is on record that *JAMES WATT* was extremely jealous for the reputation of both his patent and of his firm, for he was very quick to threaten litigation if he thought infringement was imminent. The validity of the WATT patent was only tested in court right at the end of the Century with the celebrated cases of *BOULTON & WATT* v. *BULL & BOULTON* and *BOULTON & WATT* v. *HORNBLOWER & MABERLEY* in the Court of Common Pleas in 1799.

JAMES WATT did not 'invent the steam engine' as popular historians would have it; he was a very shrewd improver who sought to gain efficiency in a prime mover that had had fifty

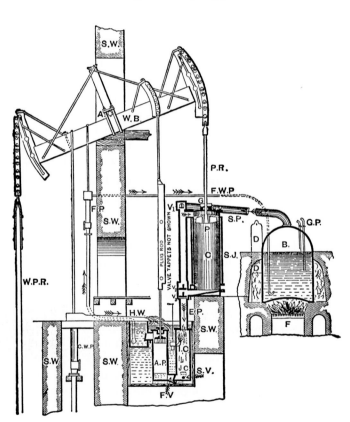

WATT'S SINGLE-ACTING ENGINE, 1769.

F	for	Furnace.	W B	for Wooden beam.
D	„	Damper.	A	„ Axis.
B	„	Boiler.	W P R	„ Weighted pump
F W P	„	Feed water pipe.		rod down to bottom of mine.
G P	„	Gauge pipes.	E P	for Exhaust pipe.
S P	„	Steam pipe.	J C	„ Jet condenser.
V_1	„	Steam valve.	I C	„ Injection cock.
V_2	„	Equilibrium valve.	C W P	„ Cold-water pump.
V_3	„	Exhaust valve.	A P	„ Air pump.
C	„	Cylinder.	S V	„ Snifting valve.
S J	„	Steam jacket.	F V	„ Foot valve.
C C	„	Cylinder cover.	D V	„ Delivery valve.
G	„	Gland and stuffing box.	H W	„ Hot well.
P	„	Piston.	F P	„ Feed pump.
P R	„	Piston rod.	S W	„ Stone work.

Diagram F.

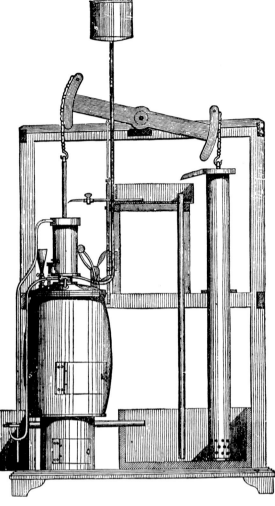

Diagram G.

years of limited success. WATT's inventions made the NEWCOMEN engine into a basically useful machine that would be capable of being developed into the ancestral unit of all of today's reciprocating engines. The story began, as legend has it, with WATT beginning his studies into steam and its properties in 1759. From the outset *JAMES WATT* approached his work scientifically and this was the basis for his success. He investigated the laws of temperature and of pressure in elastic fluids, the nature of the expansion of steam and the role of fuel in the evaporation of water. The turning point of his work came in 1763 when he was requested to repair a small model of a NEWCOMEN engine which was the property of the University of Glasgow; in attempting to set this machine to work he noted a number of deficiencies to be present and he made experiments in order to remedy them. A line drawing of this engine is shown in Diagram 'G'; the model is preserved by the University of Glasgow being on show to the General Public at the HUNTERIAN MUSEUM.

From his experimental work in science and his practical application with the NEWCOMEN model, *WATT* was able to formulate the specification contained in his patent of 1769. This described the operation of a separate condenser which revolutionised the efficiency of prime movers driven by steam.

Amongst his remedies to improve efficiency *WATT* made the following observations: –

a) That the cylinder be maintained as hot as possible and to this end he encased it with a steam jacket.
b) That the steam be condensed in a vessel remote from the cylinder.
c) Removal of air from the system.
d) Use of the expansive force of steam in the cylinder.
e) The use of oil, grease or even mercury to seal working parts instead of water.

Applying these principles *WATT* built a model of a single-acting engine as part of the 1769 Patent and this model is also preserved in the KELVINGROVE MUSEUM & ART GALLERY in Glasgow; from all of this work a single-acting, non-rotative beam pumping engine was derived, and an illustration of this machine is shown in Diagram 'F'. Whilst the engine has much in common with the NEWCOMEN type, the drawing shows the important differences which revolutionised the state of the art in the 18th Century. To work the engine it was necessary to blow through the steam, equilibrium and exhaust valves with steam to expel all of the air from the cylinder, condenser and steam piping etc. After this the equilibrium valve was shut and the injection cock was opened to create a vacuum beneath the piston and allow steam pressure to force the piston downwards. By closing the steam and exhaust valves and opening the equilibrium valve the steam forcing the piston down was allowed to go to the underside of the piston to cause it to be in equilibrium. At this point the weight of the pump rods pulled the piston to the top of the cylinder. From this stage automatic working could be maintained by the tappet rods and associated valve gear once the manual starting regime had been effective. In Diagram 'F' all of the main components of the BOULTON & WATT engine are illustrated; in particular those items introduced by *WATT* may also be seen, as follows:

a) The Steam Jacket to keep the cylinder warm.
b) The Separate Condenser which precluded cold water in the cylinder.
c) The Air Pump to draw off air and condenser water effectively.

d) The Piston, Cylinder Cover, Glands and Stuffing Boxes all properly sealed.

These together with the Cataract Governor, and the expansive working of the steam inside the cylinder enabled *WATT* to so improve the efficiency of the engine that it used but one-third of the fuel consumed by an equivalent atmospheric engine doing the same work.

This economy in the use of fuel was soon recognised by the mine owners, particularly in Cornwall, and the BOULTON & WATT units were very quickly adopted throughout the country. When BOULTON & WATT granted licences to erect their engines according to the 1769 Patent, the firm received a third part in value of any saving in fuel for each engine made to their specifications up to 1800. These royalties soon made *JAMES WATT* and his partner *MATTHEW BOULTON* very wealthy in a short space of time.

Another important component of the WATT system was the fitting of the Cataract Governor which was a simple method of regulation for the single-acting engine. This device operated in the following way: it consisted of a pump that was placed within a tank of water that was situated well below the bottom of the cylinder. The Plunger of this pump was attached to a long lever which was loaded with a heavy weight on the same side as the fulcrum of the plunger, with this lever projecting out from the other side. The tappet rod, (seen more clearly in Diagram 'F'), engaged with the lever when the piston travelled downwards and so raised the plunger of the pump. When the piston ascended again, the weight on the end of the cataract lever caused the plunger to descend and so force out the water that it had drawn in during the upward stroke.

This water was forced up through a small cock and the time occupied by the pump plunger descending depended upon the variation in the opening aperture of the cock. From this system the engine-man could control the regulation easily by opening or closing the cock to vary the number of strokes. Presumably if the cock was shut completely the water was pumped out via a by-pass pump.

As has been mentioned before in this text, there was a rash of patents concerning the 'fire-engine' in the latter half of the 18th Century and one that did cause *JAMES WATT* to think carefully was of a specification for a modified SAVERY engine filed by *WILLIAM BLAKEY* and granted Letters Patent in 1766 – this referred to oil on the surface of the water to reduce

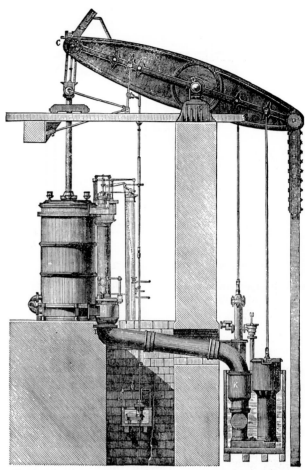

IMPROVED FORM OF WATT'S SINGLE-ACTING PUMPING ENGINE.

Diagram H.

condensation. (Brit. Pat. No. 848 of the 10th June 1766 – "Machines worked by Fire & Water with Reduced Friction Thereof"). As a result of this patent *WATT* specifically excluded all SAVERY type engines from his specifications as they did not have pistons. Another very important legal move that was made following the granting of the 1769 Patent was the 1775 Steam Engine Act. (Anno Regni Decimo Quinto Georgii III Regis). This was an Act of Parliament which vested in *JAMES WATT*, Engineer, and his Executors, Administrators and Assignees, the sole use of steam engines of his invention throughout the United Kingdom and His Majesty's Dominions for a limited length of time. The Patent and the Act made *WATT* invincible in the realms of steam engineering at that time and gave him such an overall monopoly that it would have seemed foolish to challenge it. But challenge it they did, for in 1781 *JONATHON HORNBLOWER* was granted Letters Patent for a system of compounding which is depicted in Diagram 'J'. (Brit. Pat. No. 1298 of 1781). This patent precluded WATT from using the expansion of steam in a second cylinder of greater diameter than the first. Another patent, which was

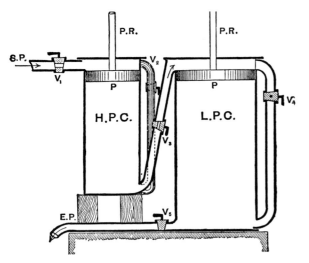

HORNBLOWER'S COMPOUND ENGINE, 1781.

S P	for Steam pipe from boiler.	V_1, V_3 for Steam cocks or valves
H P C	,, High-pressure cylinder.	V_2, V_4 ,, Equilibrium ,,
L P C	,, Low- ,, ,,	V_5 ,, Exhaust ,,
E P	,, Exhaust pipe to condenser.	

Diagram J.

granted to a mill owner named *PICKARD* in 1780 to cover the crank infuriated *WATT*, as he claimed the invention as his own but was stopped from using it! (This, of course, referred to rotative engines and is, therefore, outside the scope of this work).

JAMES WATT himself went on to patent other features of the steam engine, however, and these were as follows:-

Brit. Pat. No. 1321 of the 12th March 1782 – Expansive use of Steam, Double-Acting Engines and Compounding, Rotative Engines etc.

Brit. Pat. No. 1432 of the 28th April 1784 – Various mechanisms including the Parallel Motion, the Balance of Pump Rods, Steam Hammers, General Application of Steam Power in Mills etc., and the Application of Steam power to Carriages etc. (to which he was violently opposed!).

Brit. Pat. No. 1481 of the 14th June 1785 was a pertinent one in the present day, for *WATT* recognized the effect of pollution in the atmosphere and sought to remedy it as much as he could, for the specification calls for the introduction of "Smokeless Furnaces & Fire-places" to combat the evil. In a Patent of 1781 *WATT* had to resort to the 'Sun & Planet Motion' to circumvent *PICKARD* and in the 1782 Patent he resorted to equal diameter cylinders to effect compounding which was nowhere near as effective as the idea of *HORNBLOWER*.

The impact of *JAMES WATT* upon the whole of the industrial scene in the 18th Century was to revolutionise the ways in which people worked,

with a move from the countryside to the city, and it paved the way towards complete mechanisation which developed between the 19th and the 20th Centuries. His association with *MATTHEW BOULTON* in 1773 had important repercussions in the industry, no least of which was the setting up of the "SOHO MANUFACTORY" in Birmingham in 1774 which was the first purpose-built engine building establishment to appear. The word 'factory' came into the English language from this title. *WATT* always insisted on using the best materials available and having the best workmanship from the start; by the end of the 18th Century the elegant BOULTON & WATT engines with their cast-iron beams, parallel motion, precision valve gear and excellent polished finish and paintwork were far removed from the crude machines of the earlier part of the century.

The BOULTON & WATT Engine was adopted by many differing undertakings very soon after its fuel savings were recognized. Workshops of varying kinds, mines, waterworks and latterly iron-founders (for blast furnace blowing) invested in them and the firm became a byword for excellence. One of the first areas that *JAMES WATT* set out to conquer was Cornwall; marketing of the engine was done aggressively and *WATT* and his associates spent a considerable amount of time supervising work in the county. This tended to divert their attentions from other markets in the first instance, but as the success of the machine was broadcast other fields became open to the Partners. It must be stressed that great success was achieved in Cornwall, for between 1777 and 1801 some 52 engines were erected, of which at least two were of the rotative variety. In this period of time the NEWCOMEN Engine was effectively displaced, for by 1783 there was only one such unit in the county, and this was out of use. During the time that BOULTON & WATT were operating in Cornwall they netted a total of £180,000 in royalty payments for their work. This was done by insisting that all of the work, including that of alterations to existing engines, was to be done by the firm, their workmen or their licencees. This sum represents £88 million in today's purchasing power.

Eventually BOULTON & WATT turned their attentions to London where the price of coal was very expensive and where concerns such as waterworks could make great savings if the *WATT* system was adopted. The first engine to be supplied by the partners was to a distillery in Bow. It was erected there in 1776, this being personally overseen by *WATT* himself. *WATT* also, at that time, took the opportunity of testing various atmospheric engines

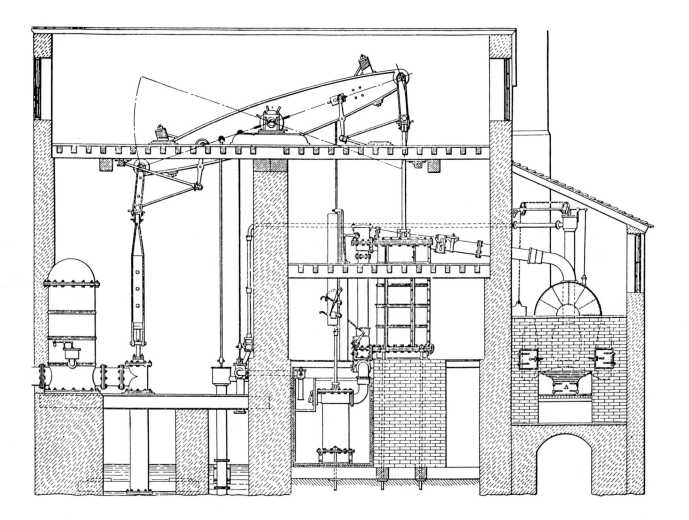

Fig. 9 - The Boulton & Watt engine erected at the Chelsea Waterworks in Pimlico, London in 1803.

in the capital to determine their average coal consumption, and to compare the results with the performance of one of his engines. Unfortunately, the progress towards the adoption of the BOULTON & WATT engine in London was not particularly swift as the water companies there were not keen on capital expenditure, despite the fact that great savings might be made in fuel costs. It was not until 1778 that a 27 ins. dia. engine having a stroke of 8 ft. was installed for waterworks use at Shadwell. In the same year another engine was erected at Chelsea and this one had a cylinder diameter of 30 ins. also by 8 ft. stroke; this engine seemed to have been of an experimental nature as it was set up for expansive working according to the provisions of the 1782 Patent and must, therefore have been the pilot exercise for that specification. *WATT* claimed the duty of 32 Millions for this engine which was very optimistic and possibly exaggerated. He ceased the use of expansive working soon after the inception of this engine. Other modifications were made to the unit including altering it to rotative working but this

proved to give it an uncomfortable, jerky motion and it soon reverted to being non-rotative. Also it was subject to a bad accident when the pump end chain broke and the piston came in-house with such force as to break the cylinder bottom, and crack the cylinder wall. A new cylinder bottom was cast locally and *WATT* managed to close up the crack in the wall. Diagram 'K' shows a section through the cylinder of this engine together with the disposition of the valves and piping. Several other BOULTON & WATT machines were supplied to London waterworks but one of the most celebrated was the single-acting engine that was built in 1803 for the Pimlico Wharf Pumping Station of the Chelsea Waterworks. This engine had a cylinder of 48 ins. diameter by 8 ft. stroke to draw water from a depth of 126 feet by means of a 17½ ins. diameter pump. It made between 13½ to 14 strokes per minute and it was capable of delivering 175 cu.ft. of water into the reservoir at each stroke; its rated horsepower was 43.2. The line drawing shown in Fig. 9 depicts the engine, which was the epitome of BOULTON &

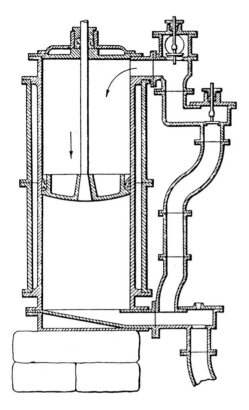

Diagram K.

WATT design and production during the lifetime of *JAMES WATT* himself. It worked successfully for a period of thirty-five years.

At the end of the 18th Century *WATT* began to perfect the double-acting principle for his engines, whereby the steam pressure acted on both sides of the piston, and a number of non-rotative pumping engines were manufactured to this design. One of the most interesting was an inverted unit, somewhat similar to a BULL engine, that was erected in 1795 at the Hallenbeagle Mine in Cornwall. The inverted cylinder, which measured 52 ins. diameter, drove directly down the shaft where it was connected to rods either side which operated two sets of pit-work. A small beam driven from a tail rod. and situated overhead. worked the air pump which was placed outside the engine-house. The original design for this engine was believed to have been drawn up by *WILLIAM MURDOCH*, *WATT's* assistant, and *WATT* himself made a drawing of it which was dated the 16th July 1795. It appears that *JAMES WATT* first considered the double-acting principle in 1774/5 when he produced a drawing to be shown to the Committee of the House of Commons; this drawing depicted a cylinder and a condenser working on that principle. The original double-acting engines made by BOULTON & WATT were rotative units but a non-rotative experimental

engine was set to work in the Soho works in 1783. This engine had a cylinder of 18 ins. diameter by 18 ins. stroke; it worked a rack and pinion system but it operated with such force that it broke the rack gear repeatedly. The first double-acting pumping engine was erected at Wheal Towan in Cornwall in 1785, being a small unit operating on the rack system as in the Soho machine. Another small engine using a different method of connection, viz. a roller and guide mechanism, was erected at Wheal Crane at more or less the same time. However, double-acting BOULTON & WATT engines followed quickly with engines being erected at Wheal Messa (42 ins. dia) with the air-pumps etc. in house, Wheal Fortune, a 45 ins. dia. engine with condensing vessel and parallel motion and the great 63 ins. Wheal Maid engine which was said to have been the most powerful prime mover in the world at the time. Another 63 ins. engine was also installed in 1798 at the Hebburn Colliery in the Durham coalfield and this reached the peak of non-rotative engine design achieved by the BOULTON & WATT firm. Despite all of these engines working on a new and, in 1783 untried design, they were all eminently successful and the double-acting principle went on to be the standard form of steam reciprocating engine down to the present day.

Notwithstanding the success of the double-acting type of engine, the single-acting engine continued to find favour with the mine engineers, and non-rotative single-acting machines were built into the 19th Century when the Cornish cycle was perfected.

After the expiry of *WATT's* patent in 1800 it seems that BOULTON & WATT concentrated on the rotative engine, for the company made a far greater number of those than of the up-and-down pumping engines; altogether the firm constructed a total of 496 engines between 1775 and 1800 when the patent expired. Of these 164 were pumping engines, 24 were blowing engines for blast furnaces and 308 for driving machinery, the latter are almost certain to have been rotative.

A number of BOULTON & WATT type engines still exist in preservation; some of the more important non-rotative units are listed below:

(1) "OLD BESS"

A non-rotative pumping engine built by *JAMES WATT* in 1777. It was initially installed to pump water at the SOHO MANUFACTORY in Birmingham. It has a cylinder dimension of 33 ins. diameter and it worked until 1848. Now located in the Motive Power Gallery in the SCIENCE MUSEUM in South Kensington, London, it is not totally complete, though most of it remains.

(2) CROFTON - Nr. Hungerford, Berkshire

Originally there were two non-rotative pumping engines manufactured by BOULTON & WATT at the CROFTON PUMPING STATION on the Kennet & Avon Canal. One was erected in 1809 and had a cylinder dimension of 36 ins., the other was installed in 1812 and had a cylinder dia. of 42 ins. with a stroke of 8 ft. driving a 30 ins. bucket pump. The 1809 engine was dismantled in 1846, whilst the 1812 unit still exists in situ, having been converted to the Cornish cycle in 1845 when it was fitted with new valve gear and drop valves, together with new pump valves. This engine can be steamed and is on view to the General Public at advertised times during the year.

(3) KEW BRIDGE - London

A BOULTON & WATT ENGINE was installed at Kew in 1839. It was previously erected in 1820 at Chelsea and is the oldest steam engine on site at the KEW BRIDGE ENGINES TRUST & WATER SUPPLY MUSEUM. There were originally two such engines here, but one was removed in 1946. This engine, like the one at Crofton, was converted to the Cornish Cycle in 1848, probably by *HOMERSHAM*. The condenser and the air-pump are original but many other parts, including the valve gear and the balance weight, date from the re-construction. The engine was first steamed by the Trust on the 8th November 1975 and the Museum is open to the General Public at advertised times.

(4) LEAWOOD PUMP - Nr. Cromford, Derbyshire

This engine was set to work in 1849 to lift water from the River Derwent to the Cromford Canal; it has a 56 ins. cylinder diameter with a stroke in the cylinder of 9 ft. 8 ins. and 10 ft. in the pump. A plunger lift pump of 56 ins. diameter raises 3½ tons of water at each stroke. The engine was constructed by GRAHAM & CO., Milton Works, Elsecar, Yorks. The general public are admitted on specified days.

(5) ASTON - Birmingham

There is a BOULTON & WATT type of engine situated on a roundabout near the site of the old Vauxhall Colliery at Aston in Birmingham. This engine was made by Messrs. GRAZEBROOK & WHITEHOUSE in about 1817 for use as a blowing engine in their foundry and steel works. This firm was noted for their work in producing material for the 'bouncing bomb' during the 2nd World War. The old engine worked well into the 20th Century and was still retained as a standby engine until the 1950's. It was erected as a monument after the closure of the firm.

(6) VARIOUS ARTEFACTS

There are many relics of the BOULTON & WATT era in various museums around the United Kingdom. The SCIENCE MUSEUM possesses a large number at South Kensington including the original model for the separate condenser. The HUNTERIAN MUSEUM at the University of Glasgow has the original NEWCOMEN model engine made by (possibly) *JOHN SISSON*, whilst the KELVINGROVE MUSEUM & ART GALLERY has a model engine used by *JAMES WATT* for his patent application in 1769. All of these artefacts are on view to the General Public at the advertised opening hours.

Fig. 10 - 'Grasshopper' type of Half-beam Cornish Engine. Side and top elevations.

CHAPTER 4: THE CORNISH ENGINE

With the expiry of the BOULTON & WATT Patent in 1800, the way was left open for designers, engineers and mine captains to improve on the steam engine generally and the non-rotative beam pumping engine in particular. Messrs. BOULTON & WATT thereafter tended to forsake Cornwall to concentrate on the rotative engine for use in factories etc. and to make components and specialities for the engine trade. A few pumping engines were installed in the West of England and a trade in waterworks engines was continued but the non-rotative engine was never a mainstay of their production in the 19th Century.

Although the BOULTON & WATT Engine had opened up the gates to economical working in Cornwall with great savings in both fuel and water being effected over the NEWCOMEN Engine, there had always been a need for continuous improvement and the WATT Monopoly had tended to stifle this need. However there were, waiting in the wings several engineers in the county whose aims were to continue the quest for economy in order to save money for the mine-owners, especially in the purchase of coal. When one thinks of the great Cornish engineers, the name of RICHARD TREVITHICK always comes to mind but, strangely, this giant of the Industrial Revolution did not have very much to do with the development of the Cornish Pumping Engine, except for improvements in boilers, for others such as ARTHUR WOOLF, the SIMS father and son, the HORNBLOWER family, the LEAN family and Messrs. HOCKING and LOAM were the real progenitors of the movement.

The initial work towards the development of the Cornish Engine was done in the last decade of the 18th Century when the WATT Patent was challenged seriously. HORNBLOWER and his associate, a Bristol iron-founder named JOHN WINWOOD, had erected a compound engine, to conform to the former's 1781 Patent, at the Radstock Colliery in Somerset which had cylinders of 19 ins. and 24 ins. but this machine did not seem to have much influence on challenging WATT. Later on another compound engine was installed by HORNBLOWER at the Tincroft Mine in 1791 and this one alarmed BOULTON & WATT, so much in fact that they persuaded their agents to distribute adverse propaganda against the system by way of articles in the press, leaflets and pamphlets. In the event, WATT did not proceed for infringement

against such a powerful rival, as an action of this sort could have had a detrimental effect upon the validity of his patent. Nevertheless, as has been mentioned earlier in this work, WATT was desperate to ensure validity of the patent, even at as late a date as 1792, so he turned his attentions to EDWARD BULL in 1793. EDWARD BULL was a clever engineer in the Cornish tradition, who had invented a compact, inverted pumping engine where the piston rod of the engine was directly connected to the pitwork. (Figs. 13 & 15). This engine possessed the virtue of saving space in the engine house, but had the disadvantage of being awkward to work upon when maintenance was needed. From 1790 to 1792 BULL and his assistant, the junior RICHARD TREVITHICK, had erected ten such machines in Cornwall before BOULTON & WATT commenced their legal action. It was unfortunate that, in the Court of Common Pleas in 1794, an injunction was made against BULL who, incidentally, was referred to as 'a stoker', restraining him from building further engines. The decision stated "that the defendant BULL's Engine was a Manifest Piracy" and this verdict was upheld finally in 1799, the year before expiry of the WATT Patent. BULL was an easy adversary and he became WATT's scapegoat to preserve the monopoly.

In the first decade of the 19th Century it was JOEL LEAN who led the way towards the development of the Cornish Engine in earnest, for his new 70" engine installed at Crowan in 1801 embodied some new ideas. The 70" cylinder was coupled to a 36" cylinder in the manner of HORNBLOWER's invention. It was fitted with plunger lift pumps instead of the old bucket type, and it drew water from the great depth of 840 feet below adit level.

Also during this decade the use of the double-acting principle increased in order that two lifts of either plunger or bucket pumps could be maintained; it was in this period that JAMES WATT built his Hallenbeagle engine and the inverted system, as envisaged by EDWARD BULL, became popular. The cast-iron beam also came into general use to supplant the common wooden unit installed universally during the 18th Century. It appeared that the first decade of the 19th Century was one of stagnation, for little of importance came to light and even the duty of the existing engines began to fall. Such a state of affairs could not continue, and the

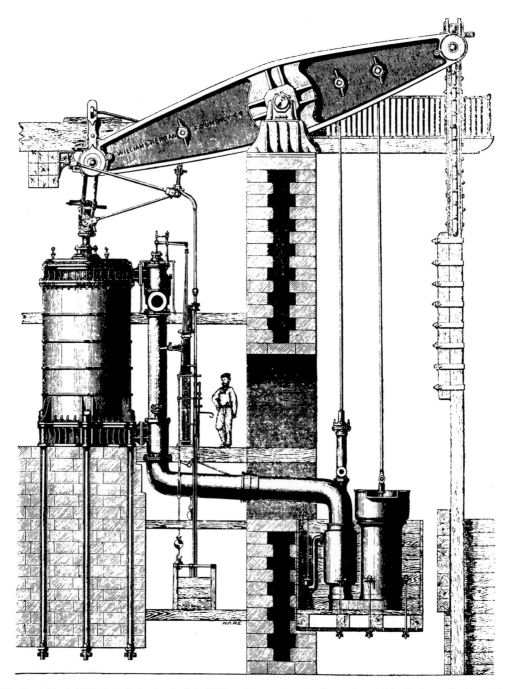

Fig. 11 - The celebrated 85" Taylor's Engine, built by Williams' Perran Foundry Co., and erected by Engineers Hocking & Loam at the "Ales & Cakes" section of the United Mines at Gewnnap.

turning point in the history of the Cornish Engine came in 1810, when a system of 'reporting' came into vogue; this system was believed to have been invented by Capt. *JOHN DAVY* who recorded the duty performed by three engines in his care at Wheal Alfred and published the results. After this *JOEL LEAN* was appointed as "Registrar & Reporter of Duty" and a publication entitled as "LEAN's Engine Reporter" was founded in 1811 to record the efficiency of pumping engines in Cornwall. The first issue reported an average duty of 15.7 millions from the results of eight engines' performance and the

journal continued in print for nearly a century.

(N.B. Excerpts from this 'Reporter' together with some of LEAN's observations were printed in book form in 1839 and re-printed in 1969 by the Truro publisher D. BRADFORD BARTON being entitled "On The Steam Engines in Cornwall").

"LEAN's Engine Reporter" was supported by another such publication later on in the 1860's, this being "BROWNE's Engine Reporter" which had a fairly short life. It is interesting to note that both of these 'Reporters' were anticipated by *HENRY BEIGHTON* who had, in 1721, made some deductions in tabular form concerning the power of NEWCOMEN Engines. These were published in "The Ladies Diary" of which he was the Editor.

The inception of "LEAN's Engine Reporter" imbued a spirit of competition between "Captains" and mine-owners, and this rivalry accelerated the race to achieve greater and greater duty, which in turn spurred engineers on to improve the performance of their engines. It was *ARTHUR WOOLF* who precipitated the efficiency revolution for, upon his return to Cornwall after a stay in London in 1811, he strove to introduce the concept of compound working with a new design of engine that he had patented. *WOOLF* filed four important patents during the first few years of the 19th Century and these have had some effect on the use of steam ever since. The first of *WOOLF's* Patents was one for an 'Improved Apparatus for Raising Steam' which was sealed in 1803. This patent (Brit. Pat. No. 2726 of 1803) really concerned boilers for industrial processing and followed the installation of some boilers into MEUX's Brewery in London. A second patent ensued in the following year and this one was more pertinent to the steam engine. It was the specification which outlined the use of compound working following some experiments with a WATT engine to which *WOOLF* had added a second or 'coupled' cylinder. This was not really a compound engine in the true sense of the word, but was a system to introduce high pressure into one cylinder whilst the other was doing the work as normal to the WATT principle. It was an important step, for the writer *JOHN FAREY* stated that *WOOLF's* name would be associated with those of *NEWCOMEN, WATT* & *TREVITHICK*, in time to come, as being one of the great steam age inventors. *WOOLF* followed up his original experiments with an improved form of engine which had a high-pressure cylinder of 8 ins. diameter by 3 ft. stroke and a low-pressure cylinder of 5 ft. stroke and 30 ins. diameter. It worked at the high pressure (for then) of 40 p.s.i. but its performance left something to be desired; although its fuel consumption was low commensurate with the power developed, the fact that imperfections in the manufacture were present meant it would not hold its pressure in the cylinder, due to leakage past. This was a problem that *WOOLF* endured until 1828, and he applied a number of solutions to overcome the nuisance which will be described later. Another factor concerning the poor performance of the experimental engine may have been the provision of incorrect ratios between the high and low pressure cylinders

resulting, perhaps, in back pressure reducing efficiency. The perennial problem of inferior materials and lack of manufacturing experience at the time had, of course, plagued all of the early pioneers.

With this second patent (Brit. Pat. No. 2772 of 1804), *WOOLF* did demonstrate a 'Law of Expansion' which he had worked out from actual experiment whereby water at boiling temperature of 212°F (100°C) only produced steam at atmospheric pressure, whereas if the temperature was raised to about 230°F (110°C) the steam would expand to 5 times its volume and provide the basis for expansive working in steam engine cylinders. *WOOLF's* 'Law of Expansion' was based upon the fact that the high-pressure engine, as invented by *TREVITHICK*, exhausted its steam to atmosphere when there was still energy left in the waste steam, which could provide more power if properly harnessed.

The problems with piston sealing discussed earlier did cause *WOOLF* some headaches after he had found that, during the experiments with the twin-cylinder engine, the hemp packing used had become badly cut away causing unsatisfactory sealing. It appeared that if WOOLF could get his ratios correct, and overcome the defects in the piston seal, his engine would be a great step forwards in the quest for greater duty. At first the remedy applied by WOOLF was a novel one for he decided to use a 'fluid metal' sealant which would always be in contact with the cylinder wall; to this end he constructed a special piston which was 30 ins. in diameter and 36 ins. deep. This piston was rebated to a diameter of 28½ ins. and to a depth of 26 ins., and into this annular space a ring of hemp packing was placed which was 7 ins. deep. Above this packing, the 'fluid metal' consisting of 3 parts tin, 3 parts of lead and 8 parts of bismuth was run in to provide the seal. This process was described in *WOOLF's* third patent, (Brit. Pat. No. 2863 of 1805) along with some other methods. Once more there was a problem – how to retain the 'fluid metal' in the annular space? This problem, together with the great weight of the special piston, far outweighed the advantages and other means were sought. 'Junk rings', used to compress the hemp packing by means of spur wheels driven by a special removable squared key, were tried as was a similar system using a nut on the piston rod to drive down the compression ring. This latter idea did work with pistons not exceeding 30 ins. in diameter. It is strange that *WOOLF* did not apparently know of the work done on piston sealing by the Rev. *EDMUND CARTWRIGHT* who patented some metallic packing

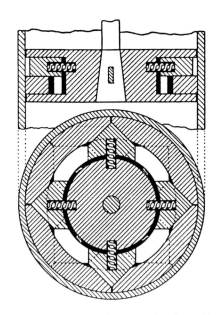

Diagram L - John Barton's segmental wedge packing.

in 1797. There was also, later on, *JOHN BARTON's* segmental wedge packing which was pressed outwards by springs and was patented by him in 1861, (Brit. Pat. No. 4062 of 1816) and shown in Diagram 'L'.

However, *WOOLF's* ideas with 'junk rings', *CARTWRIGHT's* metallic packing and *BARTON's* segmental wedges did ensure that piston sealing would be less of a bugbear in the future. Obviously, *WOOLF* did do his research in a through manner for eventually he adopted *EDMUND CARTWRIGHT's* form of packing and he modified it extensively to preclude the wear between the piston and the cylinder which had been a fault in the original system. The modifications that *WOOLF* made to ensure a true piston seal were twofold; firstly, he bored his cylinders as accurately as was possible at the time, and secondly, he arranged the springs which forced the packing outwards to push along a radial line from the piston centre. These two factors seemed to overcome piston sealing faults, and it must be assumed that *WOOLF* was so preoccupied with solving the problem in the first place that he overlooked the contribution made by *CARTWRIGHT* in the 18th Century.

At the end of his interlude in London, *ARTHUR WOOLF* had been the Engineer-in-Charge at the Griffin Brewery of Messrs. MEUX, REID & Co. where he erected an engine that operated upon his compound principles. It appears that there were some failings with this engine, for the famous engineer *JOHN RENNIE* made an adverse report about its performance, and even went as far as to suggest that the Brewery purchase a BOULTON &

WATT product to replace it. As RENNIE was on very friendly terms with the Birmingham firm it is reasonable to imagine that perhaps he had some ulterior motive. The facts were that MEUX were not happy with the performance of the engine, and the report did show that it was not performing as had been anticipated. After some modification to the cylinder ratios *WOOLF* then arranged for *RICHARD TREVITHICK* to examine and report upon the engine. *TREVITHICK* concluded that the original cylinder ratios of 23 to 1 were incorrect and that a revised ratio of 9.7 to 1 would give better performance, and also that the boiler capacity was too small for the work envisaged. The original ratios were not conducive for obtaining optimum power and perhaps *RENNIE* had been correct in his findings; later on *RENNIE* seemed to agree with *TREVITHICK's* results, particularly as regards the boiler capacity, and he stated that *WOOLF's* engine could not compete on level terms with a similar sized BOULTON & WATT unit.

Following these reports MEUX discarded *WOOLF's* engine and acquired a BOULTON & WATT, whereupon *WOOLF* resigned his post in 1808. In the end MEUX's decision proved to have been a retrograde step for it was revealed that there were some factors about the *WOOLF* engine that *TREVITHICK* did not understand concerning it – later the engineers in charge of both the WOOLF engine and the BOULTON & WATT one affirmed, in sworn affidavits, that the latter engine used more fuel for the same work and took between 20 and 21 hours to do the work that WOOLF's did in 17. This disparity was to cost Messrs. MEUX, REID & Co. some £1000 per annum more with the engine working for 9 months in the year.

Soon after this *WOOLF* went into partnership with a millwright named *HUMPREY EDWARDS* who resided at Mill Street in Lambeth. They set up an engine works in the Borough and *WOOLF* continued his calculations and designs following on from the MEUX affair. He filed his fourth and last patent during this period and this was sealed on the 9th June 1810. (Brit. Pat. No. 3346 of 1810). This patent described his latest observations on the compound system, and soon afterwards he left for Cornwall. Little has been recorded about *WOOLF's* work in Lambeth, though it is known that a number of machines of small size were made to his system there. Some were ordinary single-cylinder units whilst others were made on the compound plan. Some of the compound engines had the cylinders situated side by side and others had them placed one behind the other. This latter position was to be known as the 'tandem-compound' and, in America, traction engine manufacturers always stated that twin-cylinder tandem compound engines were "manufactured according to the WOOLF system" right up to the 1920's. *WOOLF* also substituted a

piston valve for steam distribution to replace a twin outlet cock previously used.

It was fortunate, in retrospect, that *WOOLF* had the problems with the MEUX engine, for if they had not

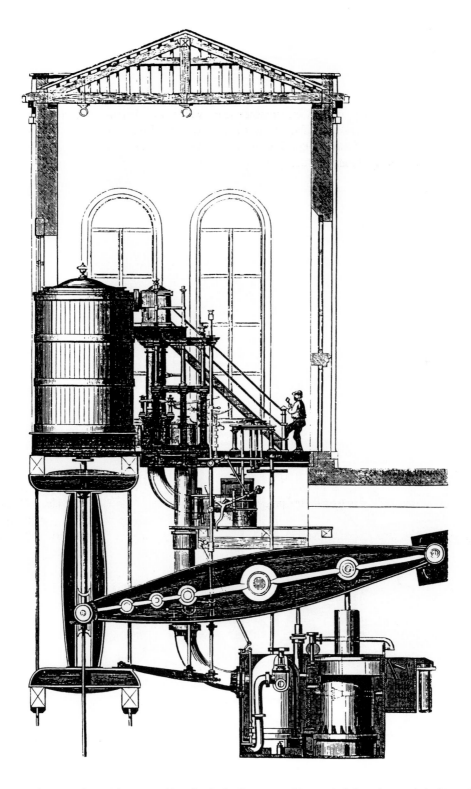

Fig. 12 - The Inverted Cornish Engine. This 86" cylinder diameter machine was built by Robert Daglish of St. Helens and erected in France at Puits Leonie in the Bouches-du-Rhone Coalfield, for the Societe Houillier et Cie.

happened he would probably never have gone on to perfect the machine as he did. WOOLF's engines were constructed with great care and there was an amount of finesse in his work that far surpassed the finish found in other makers' work; this was possibly due to the fact that during his early years he had worked with celebrated locksmith *JOSEPH BRAMAH* and the eminent engineer *HENRY MAUDSLAY*.

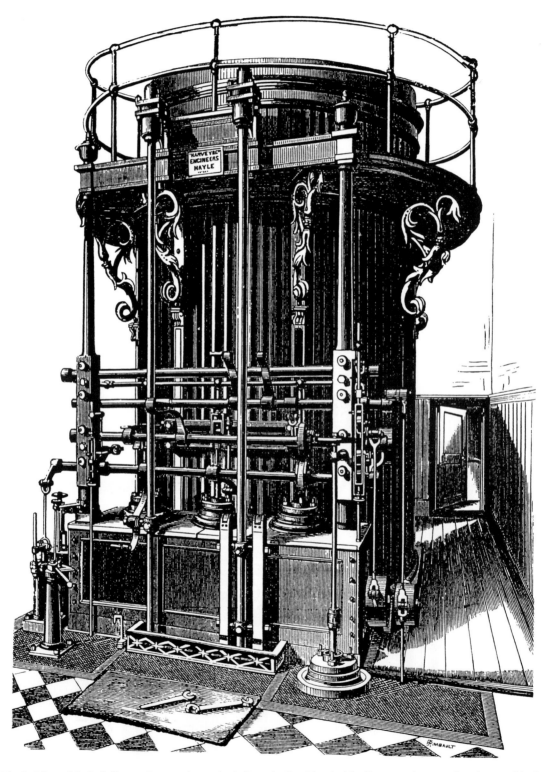

Fig. 13 - The final form of the Bull direct-action pumping engine built on the Cornish principle. Sixteen are known to have been used in Cornwall - the largest being 80 ins. diameter. In London they were erected for water works use and nine were installed during the 19th century, of which one still survives at Kew. The largest Bull engine in the capital was the great 90 ins. one set up at Campden Hill in February 1869; built by Harvey & Co, this cost £9,300 without boilers.

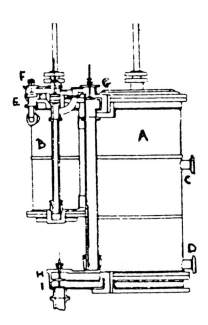

Diagram M - Woolf's compound cylinder system.

In the February of 1811 the firm of WOOLF & EDWARDS placed advertisements in the Cornish Press that stated both the superiority of their engines over the BOULTON & WATT system, and that 'WOOLF's Patent Steam Engine' was in "such a state of high perfection" that it could be worked with one half of the fuel that a comparable BOULTON & WATT unit could manage.

Some details of how the "state of high perfection" was achieved may be seen from a description of how WOOLF's compound cylinder system operated, and in Diagram 'M'. Each of the cylinders, A & B, had a steam jacket and steam was led at first into the jacket of A by the pipe at C which was in communication with the smaller cylinder. Pipe D on the low-pressure cylinder led any water or condensation back to the boiler whilst warming through. E was the pipe from the jacket to the high-pressure engine whilst F was the regulator valve. H was a valve that transferred the steam from above to below the low-pressure piston and 'I' was the exhaust valve. When the engine had been warmed through by admission of steam to the jackets, the valve at F was opened to pass steam at boiler pressure to the high-pressure cylinder; the valve at G at the same time allowed steam to pass from beneath the high-pressure piston to the upper side of the low-pressure piston, and the valve at I was opened to the condenser. All of these valves - F, G and I were opened simultaneously and, when both of the pistons arrived at the bottom, these valves were shut and a lower valve at F opened to return the steam from above to below the high-pressure piston, the valve at H doing the same to the low-pressure piston to bring the engine into

equilibrium. However, the upper valve at F could be opened or shut at will during any part of the stroke, according to engine load. Other arrangements, variations on the above theme, were also considered by WOOLF. In another system steam was made to act on the top side of the high-pressure engine piston with the under side open to condenser; the upper side of the low-pressure engine piston being always in communication with the condenser. Thus the low-pressure piston could descend in equilibrium and, when both pistons reached the bottom, the exhaust valve was shut and the steam above the high-pressure piston was sent beneath both pistons. These promptly ascended, with the topside of the low-pressure piston being open to condenser and the high-pressure piston going up in equilibrium. When both pistons had reached the top, the under side was opened to condenser, a fresh supply of steam was sent to the top of the high-pressure piston and the cycle repeated. *POLE*, in his 1844 work on the steam engine in Cornwall, stated that WOOLF's engines in Cornwall were a failure, and that *WOOLF's* ideas concerning the properties of high-pressure steam were 'ill-founded', but when one examines the performance of the engine at Wheal Abraham it is clear that this is incorrect.

During the early period of the 19th Century in Cornwall the two main protagonists were *TREVITHICK* and *WOOLF*. The former personality is well known for his work on the high-pressure engine, steam carriages for 'common roads' and for railway locomotives, but his application in Cornwall is mainly concerned with his 'Plunger Pole' engine. This type of engine, which RICHARD TREVITHICK patented in 1815, had a piston made in a similar way to the plunger of a pump and it was erected in the same way as the BULL engine, i.e. directly over the shaft. The 'Plunger Pole' was forced up by high pressure steam sometimes as high as 120 p.s.i., to haul up the pitwork and thus drain the mine. Apart from problems with imperfect castings this simple engine worked well.

TREVITHICK built his first 'Plunger Pole' engine in 1816 and it was installed in the Herland Mine. It had a single cylinder of 33 ins. diameter by 10 feet stroke. In service, however, the 'Plunger Pole' principle was an unsound concept with its defects masked by the use of high-pressure steam; having no condenser the steam was exhausted to atmosphere and therefore, energy wasted. Also rapid wear was experienced in the components of this type of engine. Alongside the *TREVITHICK* engine at the Herland Mine there was a 76 ins. engine that was built by *ARTHUR WOOLF* and both machines operated together.

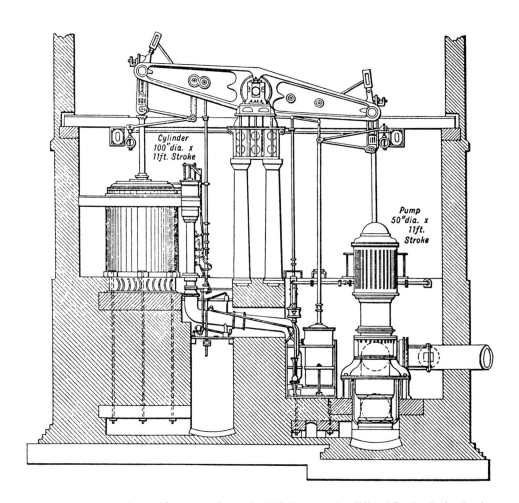

Cylinder
100"dia. x
11ft. Stroke

Pump
50"dia. x
11ft.
Stroke

Fig. 14 - A Cornish engine designed for waterworks use; the 100" Harvey engine, "Victoria" at Lee Bridge, London.

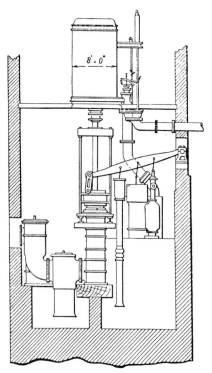

8' - 0"

*Fig. 15 - The 66" Bull engine built by Harvey
for the Hampton Waterworks.*

Unfortunately no comparative figures were ever obtained as to their respective performances; however, it is known that at Wheal Abraham mine one of *WOOLF's* engines recorded the highest duty ever noted, 56.9 millions, in May 1816. Soon after the 'Plunger Pole' experiments *TREVITHICK* sailed for South America and his influence on the Cornish scene was really terminated.

Although the Cornishmen did not take to *WOOLF's* engine in the way that its inventor would have wished, its success on the Continent was assured when *HUMPREY EDWARDS*, *WOOLF's* former partner, set up an engine works in France. A typical continental inverted *WOOLF* Compound Engine is shown in Fig. 16. Of *WOOLF's* Cornish engines the first was erected at West Wheal Fortune in 1813; another 10 h.p. engine was set to work in Marazion and this was fitted with pistons of the improved *CARTWRIGHT* pattern. *WOOLF* also built some winding engines in the county, but his first double-cylinder engine for pumping was erected at Wheal Abraham with its components being manufactured at the NEATH ABBEY IRON Co. in Wales. This one, referred to briefly above, had a high-pressure cylinder of 24 ins. by 4.3 feet stroke and a low-pressure cylinder of 45 ins diameter by 7 feet stroke. At the outset the recorded duty was dismal, being only an average of 32.6 millions, but it was discovered that a defect in casting was hampering efficiency; when this had been rectified it achieved a duty of 52.2 millions in 1815. The performance of this engine by far eclipsed that of any comparable BOULTON & WATT engine and *WOOLF's* reputation was vindicated.

Other Cornish engineers were associated with *WOOLF,* and his influence on them underscored the success of the Cornish engine world-wide, as the prime unit for the draining of mines and similar duties for nearly a century. Men such as *RICHARD JENKYN* and the *LOAM* Brothers were to become influential in the Cornish Engine sphere of activity; *JENKYN* went on to become Head Foreman at HARVEYS HAYLE FOUNDRY and, later on, was appointed as the Engineer at the nearby COPPERHOUSE FOUNDRY. *MATTHEW* and *MICHAEL LOAM* became respected engineers in Cornwall, with the latter being *WOOLF's* personal assistant and eventually taking over most of his mentor's work. Other notable individuals were the father and son partnership of *WILLIAM* and *JAMES SIMS* and the firm of HOCKING & Son. *JAMES SIMS* is associated with the further development of the compound engine and patented his system in 1841. (Brit. Pat. No. 8942 of the 29th April 1841). A notable example of his work, replacing a BOULTON & WATT engine of 1809, was installed at Crofton Pumping Station on the Kennet & Avon Canal in 1846. *See APPENDIX 'A'* (The engine at CROFTON designed by *SIMS*

is now altered to the classic HARVEY & CO. Cornish style of operation).

The work of all of these pioneers in Cornwall had the effect of producing a form of engine which was pre-eminent throughout the world during the 19th and early 20th Centuries for pumping services. Engines of the Cornish type were produced extensively for use at home both in mines and waterworks and also for export all over the globe. HARVEYS HAYLE FOUNDRY, SANDYS & VIVIAN'S COPPERHOUSE FOUNDRY and WILLIAMS' PERRAN FOUNDRY at Perranporth built units up to a cylinder diameter of 112 ins. for

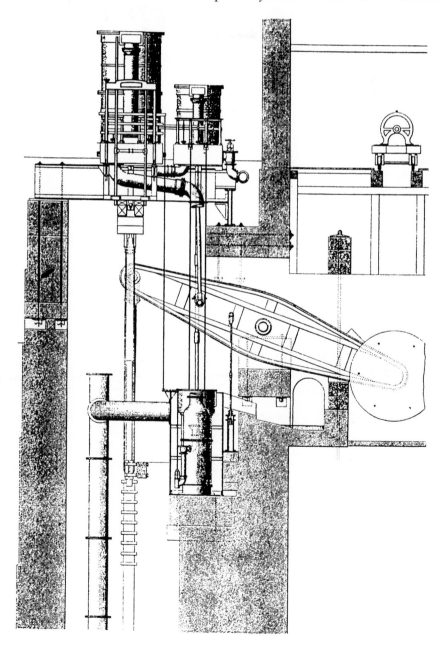

Fig. 16 - The inverted form of Woolf Compound engine as favoured on the Continent. This engine was probably made in France by Humprey Edwards, the one-time partner of Arthur Woolf.

England and a massive 144 ins. engine built by HARVEY for Holland. This form of working became known as the 'Cornish Cycle' and it incorporated all of the improvements made by *WATT, TREVITHICK, WOOLF* and the others and remained as a standard well into the 20th Century.

The Operation of the Cornish Cycle:

In Diagram 'N', which is representative of the standard Cornish single-acting pumping engine cylinder, the steam passed into the cylinder through valve **A** and acted upon the top of the piston to force it down with valve **B** being closed. The space below the piston at that time was in communication with the condenser via the valve at **C**. At the end of the down stroke, the valve **B** opened to exhaust with the valves **A** and **C** being closed, allowing the steam to pass from above the piston to the space below it through valve **B** and not directly to the condenser; then the piston ascended in equilibrium. The economy achieved using the Cornish Cycle was attained by the fact that the clearance surface above the piston was never put into direct communication with the condenser, which permitted the range of temperature above the piston being from admission (of steam) to release only. Below the piston, the range of temperature was from release to exhaust, with the fall of temperature from the admission of

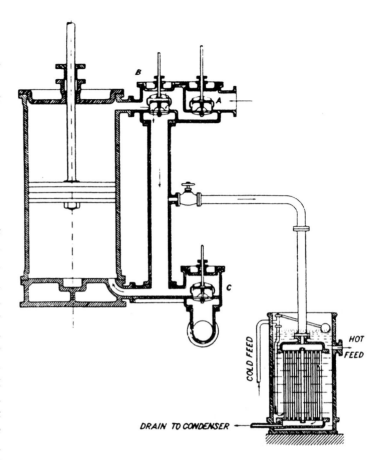

Diagram N - The Cornish Cycle; operation.

the steam until it was exhausted thus occurring in two stages. A part of the Cornish system that was unique was the Cornish 'Double-Beat' or 'Crown' valve; this is illustrated in Diagram 'O' and was used as an equilibrium valve, and also in place of the standard slide valve for the admission and exhausting of steam. In the diagram, the Crown **C** is connected to its spindle **S** by means of a cotter which enabled it to be lifted or lowered on to its two seats, identified as **VS1** and **VS2**. The upper seat was secured to the valve chest **VC** by a bolt **B**, which screwed into a clamp **C1**, whilst the lower seat was driven by an interference fit into the base of the chest. The arrows shown indicate the direction in which the gas or fluid travelled. The advantage of this valve was that it only required half the lift of an ordinary single seated valve.

The CORNISH ENGINE* was manufactured in several forms, as follows:

a) Normal with cylinder inverted, and beam overhead. (Single & Double-acting•)

b) Inverted with piston acting downwards, and beam below. (Single & Double-acting•)

c) *BULL* with cylinder directly set over the pump rods. (Single-acting only)

d) *WOOLF/HORNBLOWER* Compound with

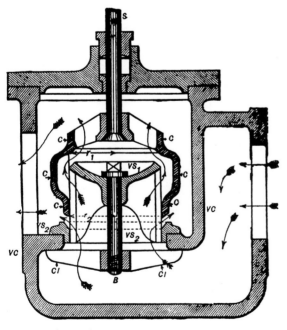

Diagram O - The Cornish Double-beat, or Crown Valve.

cylinders side by side on one side of the beam. (Single & Double-acting•)

e) **Half-beam or 'Grasshopper'** – Single expansion and compound.

f) *HATHORN DAVEY* **Compound** inverted with each cylinder either side of the beam.

Cornish engines are always described by cylinder diameter, i.e. a 100 ins. engine, and the stroke is sometimes quoted twice. This latter refers to the first figure quoting the actual engine stroke and the second the pump stroke in the sump.

Note that double-acting engines are not the classic Cornish Cycle but are adaptations thereof.

Over a period of time encompassing the first half of the 19th Century many of the aforementioned workers filed patents to protect their ideas – of these four patents were sealed by *ARTHUR WOOLF*, and seven by *RICHARD TREVITHICK*, of which the most important was the British Patent No. 3992 of the 6th June 1815, which described his high-pressure steam engine. *JAMES SIMS* sealed a further patent concerning his system, this being British Patent No, 11859 of the 9th September 1847.

CORNISH ENGINES in PRESERVATION:

1) KEW BRIDGE WATERWORKS - London

This is the most important concentration of CORNISH engines in the world and it houses engines of different types; most of the engines are operated at regular intervals, and the museum is open to the public all year round.

The East Engine Room has a BOULTON & WATT engine modified to work on the Cornish Cycle.
The West Engine Room houses an engine similar to the BOULTON & WATT and also modified to the Cornish principle. It was built in 1837 by MAUDSLAY, SONS & FIELD of Lambeth.
The 90 and 100 Inch Engine Room house a 90 ins. Cornish Engine designed by *THOMAS WICKSTEED* and made by the COPPERHOUSE FOUNDRY. The adjacent 100 ins. engine was built by HARVEY & Co. in 1869 and they are two of the largest beam engines in the world.
Near the West Engine Room is the sole surviving BULL Engine in the world (See Fig. 13). This was built by HARVEY in 1859. It is of 70 ins. dia. by 10 ft. stroke and worked until 1944.

2) EAST POOL & AGAR - Redruth, Cornwall

The 90 ins. TAYLOR Engine was designed by *NICHOLAS TRESTRAIL* and was originally set to work at Highburrow East Shaft in 1893. It was re-erected on its present site in 1924 and ceased work on the 28th September 1954. It was saved for preservation by *GRENVILL BATH* of Florida, U.S.A. and is now in the care of the NATIONAL TRUST. Built by HARVEY & Co. the engine has a 10 ft. engine stroke and a 9 ft. pump stroke. It is on view to the General Public.

3) SOUTH CROFTY - Camborne, Cornwall

Near to the TAYLOR engine is the ROBINSON's 80 ins. engine which was started in June 1885 at Alfred Consols. Designed by *SAMUEL GROSE* it was built by the COPPERHOUSE FOUNDRY. After many moves it was re-erected on its present site in 1903. It last worked in 1955 but, although preserved and still on site, this is not open to the General Public.

4) PRESTONGRANGE - Nr. Edinburgh

Another HARVEY & Co. engine that was installed in its present position in 1874. It drives 3 pumps made by ANDREW BARCLAY & Sons Ltd. installed in 1905. It worked until 1954 and is now preserved as part of the LADY VICTORIA COLLIERY Mining Complex Museum. Open to the General Public.

5) NANTLLE - Wales (Dorothea Slate Quarry)

A Cornish pumping engine built by HOLMAN Bros. of Cambourne and designed by *NICHOLAS TRESTRAIL* in 1904. On standby until 1956. Not open to the public, but earmarked for preservation.

6) COLD HESLEDON - Sunderland

Two Cornish engines built by DAVEY Bros. of Sheffield in 1879 – worked until 1942. Believed still in situ, but in private ownership.

7) CRUQUIUS - Holland

Built by HARVEY & Co. in the 1840s, this engine, together with two others, were designed to drain the Harlemmere. Said to be the largest steam engine ever built, Cruquius has been preserved by the Dutch Government and is open to the public. It is an annular compound of 84/144 ins. and the low-pressure cylinder is operated by four rods. Eight lattice beams radially disposed from the piston rods operated 84 ins. bucket pumps. Last run in June 1933, it is now moved hydraulically. One of the trio, the van Lijnden Engine, was built by the PERRAN

FOUNDRY and designed by *A. DEAN & J. GIBBS.*

8) CROFTON - Nr. Hungerford, Berkshire

A SIMS Combined Cylinder Engine was installed at Crofton to replace the 1809 BOULTON & WATT, dismantled in 1846. This engine was not successful and the existing No. 1 engine was left to carry on after it had been converted to the Cornish cycle. However, in 1903 a new 42-inch cylinder was fitted to the engine and it was altered by HARVEY & Co. to the classic single cylinder Cornish Cycle being known as CROFTON No. 2 Engine. It remained in service until 1952. Open to the General Public at advertised times.

9) PARKANDILLICK CLAYWORKS - St. Austell, Cornwall

This engine is preserved by ENGLISH CHINA CLAYS on site. It was built by the COPPERHOUSE FOUNDRY of Hayle in 1852 for use at Wheal Kitty at St. Agnes. In 1912 it was moved to its present location and fitted with a new cylinder by BARTLE'S FOUNDRY of Carn Brea. It is a 50-inch engine with a stroke of 10 ft. in the cylinder and 9 ft. in the shaft. Accessible by prior arrangement only.

10) GOONVEAN CLAYWORKS - St. Austell,

At the time of writing this engine is still on site but is inaccessible due to the danger of a collapsing shaft nearby. It is in private ownership. The engine is a 50-inch Cornish cycle unit manufactured by HARVEY & Co. of Hayle for Penhalls Mine in 1863. It was moved in 1899 to a site at Gooninnis and thence in 1910 to its present location. Standard HARVEY type with two plug rods with 10ft. stroke in the cylinder and 9 ft. in the shaft.
(Notes kindly supplied M. EVANS, GOONVEAN Ltd.)

11) POLDARK MINING MUSEUM -Helston, Cornwall

This engine was situated at the GREENSPLAT CLAYWORKS near St. Austell. It is a small, 30-inch machine which is open to the General Public at advertised hours. Apparently the manufacturer of this engine is not known, as no makers plate or other identification exists. It has a 9 ft. stroke in the cylinder and an 8 ft. stroke in the shaft. It is now operated by compressed air and it was the last Cornish Pumping engine to operate commercially.

12) CARPALLA CLAYWORKS ENGINE
(Now in store at the Reserve Collection of the SCIENCE MUSEUM, Wroughton)

This engine was built by HARVEY & Co. in 1863. It originally worked at the WEST POLBREEN MINE , and was then moved to the WEST KITTY Mine at St. Agnes. Finally it was taken to a site alongside the Newquay to St. Austell Road owned by CARPALLA CLAYWORKS. It is a 40-inch engine with an equal beam stroke of 9 ft. This is a classic mid 19th Century HARVEY & Co. product; it has two plug rods and standard HARVEY valve gear, though a top handle cataract has been added at a later date. It is possible that it may be re-erected on the site of HARVEY's Foundry at Hale as a monument to that enterprise.

13) SEVERN TUNNEL PUMPING ENGINES

Two BULL 50-inch Pumping Engines built by HARVEY & Co. were installed between 1876 and 1877, to start work in 1878. Both of them have 10 ft. stroke and 26 inch pumps. They were positioned at Sudbrook on the Monmouth side of the tunnel, and they were in constant work until 1954, finally ceasing on the 6th November 1962. Today one is held in the reserve store of the Science Museum at Wroughton, whilst the other is held by the National Museums and Galleries of Wales in Cardiff.
(Information concerning Reserve Collection engines kindly supplied by B. RUSSELL, Assistant Curator, The Science Museum).

14) "THE GIANT GRASSHOPPER" -The Wirral

A massive compound half beam engine at the Shore Road Pumping Station in the Wirral, which was installed to draw water from the Mersey rail tunnel. Both the engine and its pumps were built by ANDREW BARCLAY & SONS LTD. of Kilmarnock. The engine made 3 strokes per minute and drew water from a depth of 180 ft. It has a 36 ins. H.P. bore, by 13 ft. stroke. The beam is 32ft. 6 ins. long between centres, and the pump, no longer in-situ, was 40 ins. bore by 15 ft. stroke. The engine's weight is 262 tons, and it is open to the General Public.

15) WOODHOUSE BEAM ENGINE - Springhead Pumping Station, Kingston-upon-Hull

This engine was preserved by KINGSTON-UPON-HULL CORPORATION WATER DEPT. in 1957 after working from 1876 until 1952. It formed the basis of a museum which is now closed. It has a cylinder diameter of 90 ins. and a stroke of 11 ft, two 27 ins. diameter bucket pumps and one ram pump of 36 ins. diameter with a total lift of 150 ft. It was built by HELLIS-LIGHTFOOT of Millwall. It is not open to

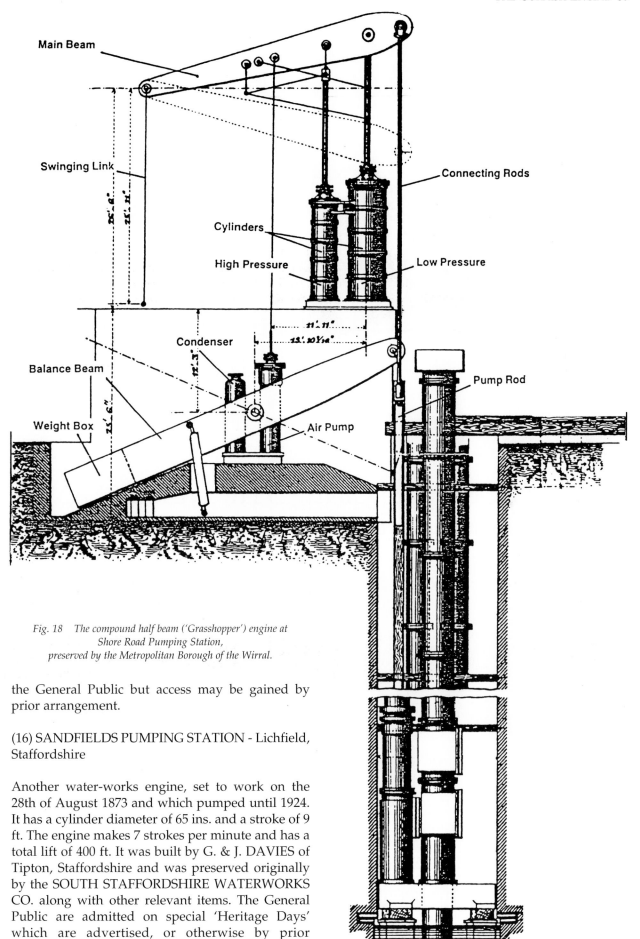

Main Beam

Swinging Link

Connecting Rods

Cylinders

High Pressure

Low Pressure

Condenser

Balance Beam

Weight Box

Air Pump

Pump Rod

*Fig. 18   The compound half beam ('Grasshopper') engine at
Shore Road Pumping Station,
preserved by the Metropolitan Borough of the Wirral.*

the General Public but access may be gained by prior arrangement.

(16) SANDFIELDS PUMPING STATION - Lichfield, Staffordshire

Another water-works engine, set to work on the 28th of August 1873 and which pumped until 1924. It has a cylinder diameter of 65 ins. and a stroke of 9 ft. The engine makes 7 strokes per minute and has a total lift of 400 ft. It was built by G. & J. DAVIES of Tipton, Staffordshire and was preserved originally by the SOUTH STAFFORDSHIRE WATERWORKS CO. along with other relevant items. The General Public are admitted on special 'Heritage Days' which are advertised, or otherwise by prior arrangement.

The Cruquius Engine - The Netherlands

(almost certainly the world's largest steam engine)

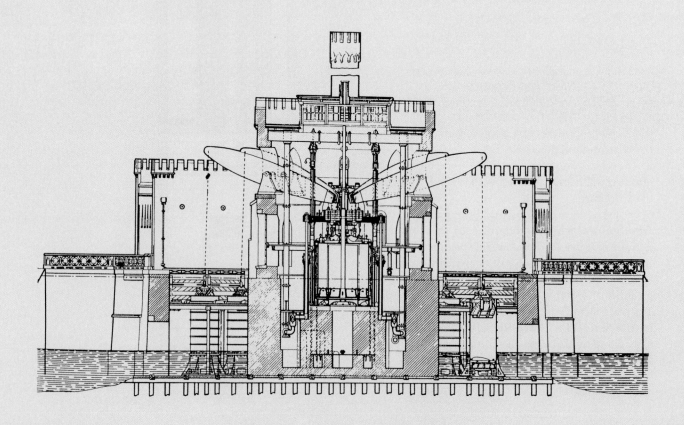

Built, along with two others, to drain the Harlemmere during the 1840s, this massive annular compound pumping engine has a low-pressure cylinder of 144 ins. in diameter, with an 84 ins. high-pressure cylinder within it.

The colossal engine house is shown (top right). Five of the eight lattice beams, which operated 84 ins. pumps to drain the Mere through the semi-circular sluices, can be seen.

The valve gear is shown top left, and the top nozzles can be seen in the photograph above left. The valve gear is positioned above the cylinder cover, and not at the side, as was usual with standard engines. Note the four piston rods fixed to the annular compound low pressure cylinder.

At 144 ins. in diameter, the low-pressure cylinder was the largest ever cast for a Cornish and, quite possibly, any other engine.

The preserved pumping station is open to the public, and the engine is turned over, by hydraulic power rather than steam.

KEW BRIDGE - LONDON
(the world's largest collection of Cornish Engines)

 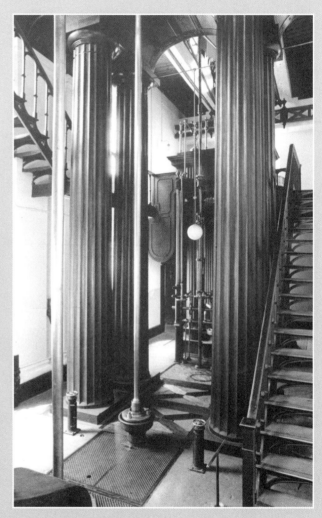

The Controls of two of the cornish engines at Kew Bridge - the 65" Maudslay on the left, and the 90" 'Grand Junction on the right.

The 65" Maudslay engine was built in 1838 and worked at Kew Bridge Pumping Station until 1942. It was restored to working order in 1985.

Whilst this is not a very large engine, the man standing on the nozzle level platform gives an indication of just how large even an intermediate size Cornish Engine is.

The engine's beam is visible at the top centre of this photograph.

Built by Harvey & Co. of Hayle in 1846, the 90' 'Grand Junction' is the largest working Cornish Engine in the world.

This engine is 35 feet high - the platform that can be seen at the top of the photograph is an intermediate one giving access to the tops of both the cylinder, and the valve gear.

The care taken to ensure the aesthetic harmony of the engine is clear.

The top nozzles of the 90" 'Grand Junction' Engine. One end of the beam can be seen at top right, and the weight bob on the pump rod may just be made out below the two right hand windows.

Standing alongside the 90' engine at Kew is the even larger 100" engine which is currently inoperable.

The photograph at left shows the Beam of this engine from the pump end.

The massive construction, and bracing of this beam can be compared with that of the 90" inch, shown overleaf.

The blocks on which the beam's end is resting are to support the beam and relieve excess stresses on the structure. They would be removed when the engine was working.

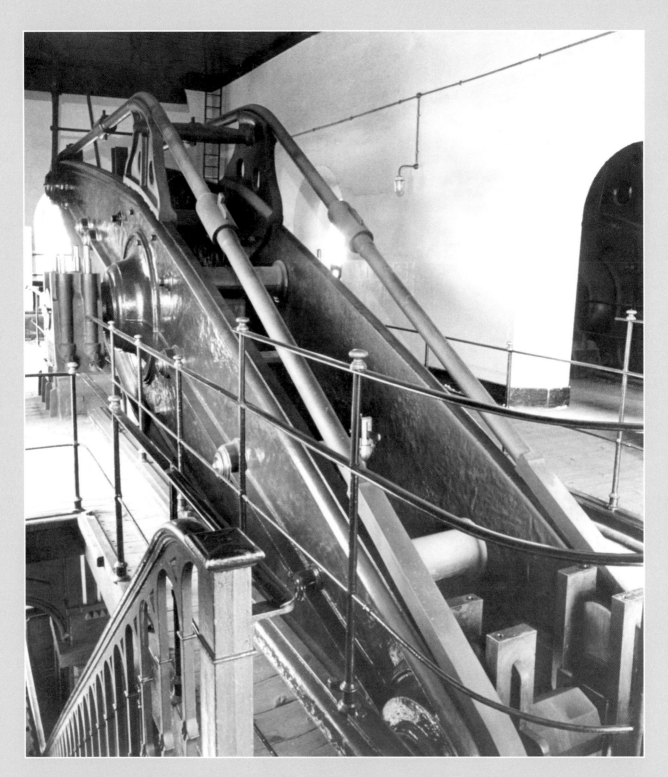

The beam of the 90" 'Grand Junction' Engine. This photograph is taken from the pump end of the Beam, which weighs 35 tons.

The slightly lighter construction, compared with the 100" engine's Beam, which can just be made out through the arch, will be noted.

Pumping engines generally ran continuously, and the engine-man's assistant would have to ride the moving Beam to lubricate parts on, or within, the Beam itself.

All Kew Bridge photographs reproduced courtesy of Kew Bridge Steam Museum

A number of different types of boiler were used at different times on Cornish engines, from the earliest days up to the 20th Century. At first a primitive style of steam raiser known as the 'balloon' or 'beehive' boiler was used on the NEWCOMEN Engines. These consisted of a vertical cylindrical vessel with a concave bottom above the fire. The top of the cylinder was mounted by a leaden dome that was hemispherical in shape. The main part of the boiler was fashioned from copper plates. These boilers were only good enough for pressures of up to 5 p.s.i.

The 'Balloon' boiler was eventually phased out in favour of the 'Waggon' boiler invented by *JAMES WATT* and illustrated in Diagram 'N'. This type of boiler was so named because of its resemblance to a covered Waggon. The Waggon boiler was a great advance upon the earlier type and it possessed many ingenious features. In construction the top was convex, the bottom concave and the sides were sometimes flat and sometimes concave. In smaller sizes of this boiler the fire heated the water beneath the barrel and then the gases passed along the lateral flues along one side of the barrel across the front end and back alongside to be discharged up the chimney. This method of conducting the gases was known as 'wheel-draught' since it allowed the gases to travel right around the boiler barrel. In the larger sizes BOULTON & WATT used a central flue to augment the flow and in this variety return was made via the flue.

A novel method of damping and regulating pressure was used. The column of water in the vertical pipe formed the pressure gauge and the damper was controlled by the rise and fall in this column (shown on the left of the drawing). The water level in the boiler was regulated by a float which followed the water level in the boiler – in falling it opened a valve in the vertical feed pipe which admitted water, whilst in rising it closed the valve. This arrangement was only useful for pressures up to 10 p.s.i.

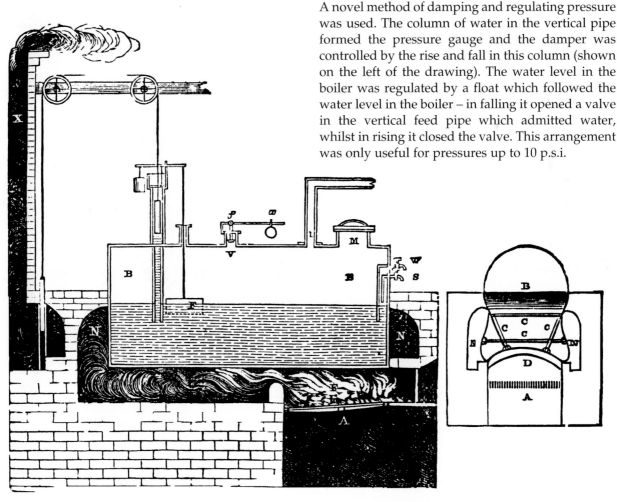

B	for Boiler		M for Man hole.	
A	,, Fire-grate.		V	Safety Valve.
N	Lateral flues.		F	Float.
S and W	Steam and Water cocks.		X	Chimney

Diagram P - James Watt's 'Waggon' Boiler.

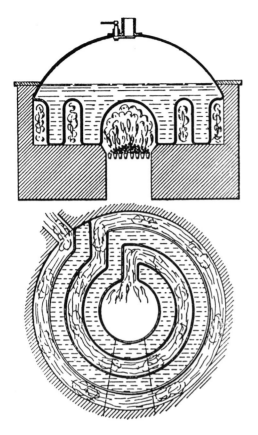

Fig.19 - Stephen & Hadley's Patent 'Haystack' Boiler.

its shape – a cylinder with hemispherical ends – but being unstayed, it was prone to explosion if forced by the firemen. One strange development was that of the 'Moorstone' boiler which was constructed from blocks of granite arranged in a boiler shape. Some blocks from one of these survive.

Another novel style of boiler is shown in Fig. 20. This unit was made entirely from cast-iron and was often supplied with engines made by *ARTHUR WOOLF*. The 'Haystack' and the WOOLF boilers were only good for about 15 p.s.i. whilst the egg-ended boiler could only support 20 p.s.i. if used properly.

Following on from all of these early boilers, most of which left something to be desired, was the archetypal 'Cornish' Boiler with the single flue that is depicted in Figs. 21, 22 & 23. It was invented by *FRANCIS TREVITHICK* and it revolutionised steam production for it could easily maintain pressures of 80 p.s.i. plus. The Cornish boiler was to become the norm for industrial use in the 19th and 20th centuries, along with its "cousin" the 'Lancashire' boiler.

A boiler that pre-dated the Cornish boiler was *RICHARD TREVITHICK's* High-pressure boiler which was also capable of a good performance,

The 'Waggon' type was in general use in Great Britain up to about 1830 when it was supplanted by other more suitable steam generators. One of these was STEPHEN and HADLEY's patent 'Haystack' Boiler which was described in British Patent No. 634 of 1748. In the drawing shown in Fig. 19 the configuration is revealed, together with the path of the hot gases. Another boiler in use after the waggon type was the 'Egg-ended' a boiler which could take higher pressures by reason of

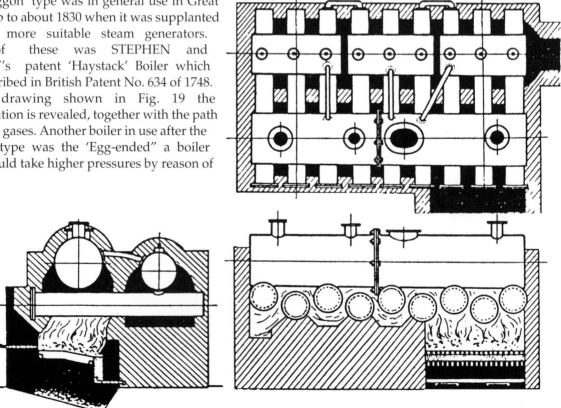

Fig. 20 - Arthur Woolf's Patent Cast-iron Boiler.

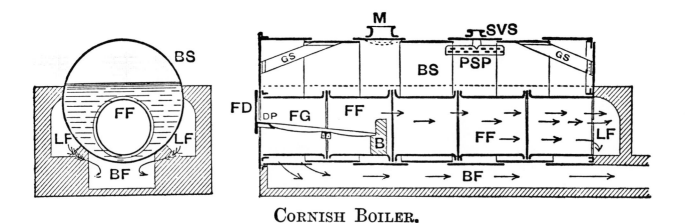

CORNISH BOILER.

BS represents the Boiler shell.
F F   ,,   ,,   Furnace flue.
F G   ,,   ,,   Fire-grate.
D P   ,,   ,,   Dead plate.
B   ,,   ,,   Bridge.
F D   ,,   ,,   Fire door.
L F   ,,   ,,   Lateral or side flues.

B F   represents the Bottom flue to chimney.
G S   ,,   ,,   Gusset Stays.
M   ,,   ,,   Manhole.
S V S   ,,   ,,   Safety valve seat.
P S P   ,,   ,,   Perforated Steam Pipe.

Fig. 21 - Sectional side and end elevations of a typical Cornish Boiler as used in the 19th & 20th Centuries.

Fig. 22 - a typical Cornish Boiler of the mid 19th century, as supplied by Williams' Perran Foundry Co.

Fig.23 - two Cornish Boilers in tandem.

illustrated in Fig. 23. It is said that the elder *TREVITHICK* managed to exceed 100 p.s.i. with one of these when used with his 'Plunger Pole' engines, but this may have been exaggeration on his part, for he also claimed a duty of 'nearly 100 millions' for his engine – a claim that was patently impossible.

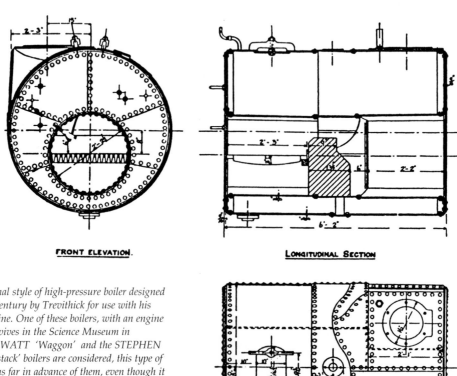

FRONT ELEVATION.

LONGITUDINAL SECTION

Fig. 24 - The original style of high-pressure boiler designed early in the 19th Century by Trevithick for use with his 'Plunger Pole' engine. One of these boilers, with an engine mounted on it, survives in the Science Museum in London. When the WATT 'Waggon' and the STEPHEN & HADLEY 'Haystack' boilers are considered, this type of steam generator was far in advance of them, even though it was invented at the dawn of the 19th Century.

CHAPTER 6: PITWORK, PUMPS AND OTHER APPARATUS.

Initially the NEWCOMEN Engine, the BOULTON & WATT Engine and, latterly, the CORNISH Engine were developed for the purpose of draining mines, but later on other uses were found for them in connection with mining and urban waterworks. The primary use of the non-rotative beam engine had always been for pumping water and this activity was eventually divided into two directions, viz., in the de-watering of mines and for the provision of water in large conurbations. Other uses were found for the up-and-down motion of the engine and these consisted of raising ore and personnel from the depths of mineshafts.

Some details of the various tasks that these engines had to perform are given hereunder:

MINE PUMPING:

One of the greatest problems associated with mining was the removal of water that infiltrated into shafts and adits and which hindered the operation due to excess flooding; to this end the introduction of the pumping engine during the 18th Century was a tremendous boon to the Mine Captain. In theory, the action of pumping was a simple one, in that the pumprods, known as 'pitwork', and always made from wood (best RIGA Pine), extended down from the beam of the engine to the base of the shaft where a pump was situated in a sump where water tended to gather. This pump, right at the bottom, was of the bucket-lift type and it was fitted with an 'egg-ended' perforated rose or 'windbore' which was submerged within the sump; the main barrel of the pump was fitted with a clack or flap valve which remained on its seat by gravity. A bucket was suspended on rods and this possessed valves which opened on the downwards stroke and which were forced shut on the upwards stroke in order to form a vacuum. The action of pumping was thus; the bucket descended with its valves open and the clack shut, when it began to ascend suction opened the clack valve and the bucket valves shut to lift a quantity of water, (usually about 30 Imperial Gallons) upwards to be emptied into a cistern at the first stage. This lowest stage was emptied by another type of pump which was known as the 'plunger pole' and this raised the water to another cistern higher up the shaft and so on. A series of these plunger lifts sent the water up the shaft with each stroke transmitting an equal quantity of water to that displaced by the plunger pole itself. (Figs. 26 to 30). The reality of this system

was not as simple as it seemed for, as mines became deeper, the pressure required to raise the water increased proportionally with the depth of the shaft rising to about 300 p.s.i. at 300 feet which was, then, regarded as the maximum that the cast iron pipes of the period could withstand. To this end the need for the installation of the plunger poles was necessitated at intervals less than 300 feet and with mines in Cornwall reaching depths of 1000 ft. it was apparent that several stages were required. One South Australian mine was over 2500 ft. deep and there about eight plunger pumps, plus the sump bucket lift, were needed.

It was clear that the weight of the pitwork and pump buckets etc. was considerable, particularly in deep shafts, and in shafts of 1000 feet this could amount to some 43 tons, but the weight of the rods, plungers and other equipment could be near to about 100 tons and, therefore it was imperative that a 'balance bob' (Fig. 31) was fitted to equalize the weight. These 'bobs' were situated at ground level or just below, but other smaller balances could also be found under ground, to minimise stress in the rod and preclude the possibility of failure in the system. In coal mines with horizontal seams the shaft was usually vertical and the pitwork was simple but in the mining of ore, as in Cornwall, the lodes in the hard rock were inclined with the result that shafts changed angle as the lode was traced downwards. These changes in direction caused the need for apparatus to 'break the angle' and one or two methods to achieve this were employed; one was the use of the 'Angle or V-Bob' (Fig. 32) which, although costly to install, was the most frequently used method, with this coming in two forms – the 'fend-off' bob was installed on the inside of the shaft and the 'tie-back' on the outside bend. Another method was by means of 'dolly-wheels' which followed the trace of the bend in three stages; before, at point of bend, and after. This method was cheap to fit but was inferior to the angle-bob system. A third system was the 'pin-chain' which also necessitates three wheels attached to the side of the shaft over which ran a chain – this required constant maintenance and renewal and often was lubricated by a constant fall of water. The final solution to this problem was the 'gusset-filler' which consisted of a triangular gusset fitted at the point of bend on the pitwork with a bush installed some way above to hold the pitwork central, a wheel to run in the gusset and a jockey wheel some way down to locate the pitwork past the

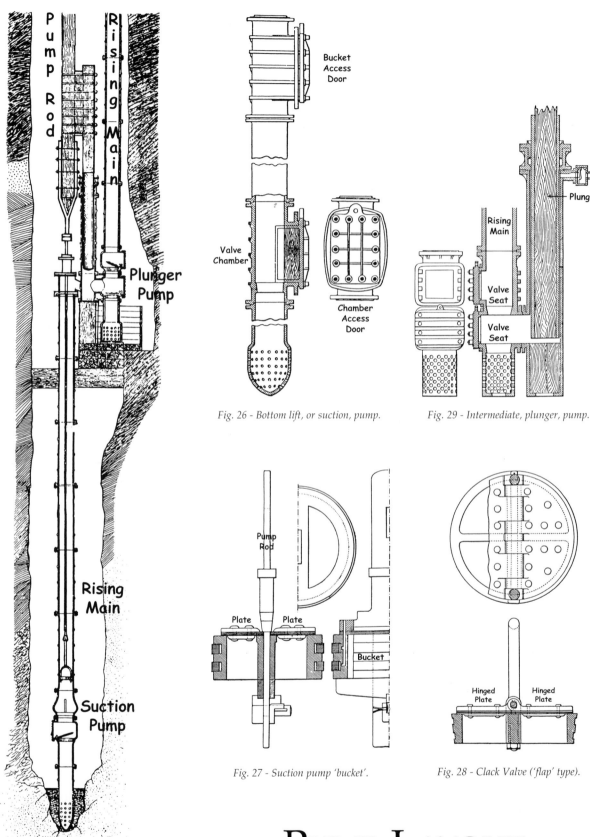

Fig. 26 - Bottom lift, or suction, pump.

Fig. 29 - Intermediate, plunger, pump.

Fig. 27 - Suction pump 'bucket'.

Fig. 28 - Clack Valve ('flap' type).

Fig. 30 - Cornish pump layout, showing the lift (suction) pump at bottom, and the intermediate (plunger) stage at upper right.

PUMP LAYOUT
AND COMPONENTS

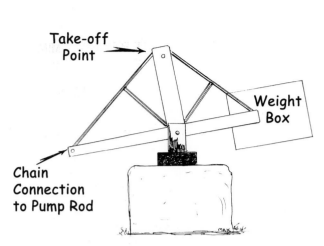

Fig. 31 - Balance Bob - Schematic drawing.

Fig. 32 - A V Bob. This was mounted in a recess in the shaft wall, pivoted by the large bearing on the right with the pump rod being attached to the other ends which protruded into the shaft.

angle; this system entailed considerable friction in operation.

With the complexity and expense associated with deep shaft mining in Cornwall, if the mine was situated on a cliff edge or on a prominence, a side tunnel or 'adit' would be driven from the lowest open location in order to intersect the main shaft to facilitate natural drainage as far as possible, and to allow the engine to 'pump to adit' only, making a great saving in fuel and maintenance costs. The *Great County Adit* in Gwennap Parish near Falmouth had a series of such adits some 40 miles in length.

WATERWORKS PUMPING:

The ever-increasing population in large cities posed the problem of effective sanitation following frequent epidemics of cholera and other waterborne diseases. In London, which was the largest city in the world in the middle of the 19th Century, the problem was appalling with the River Thames and its tributaries being nothing more than open sewers; the odour was so bad that even sittings of Parliament had to be abandoned during the summer months because of the smell nearby. Action was soon taken and under the supervision of the eminent engineer *Sir JOHN BAZALGETTE* a series of works was undertaken to collect and handle sewage and to provide safe drinking water for the populace. This great system became the prototype for similar schemes around the world. The great holding tank and the concentration of rotative beam engines at Crossness as well as the collection of non-rotative engines at Kew were all a part of this monumental vision. A series of pumping stations were set up all over London and most of these used the CORNISH engine of a special type which had huge weights applied on the pump side of the beam, in place of the pitwork used in mines, for the pumping depths were much less and the need to carry the beam over centre had to be enhanced.

LAND DRAINAGE:

The CORNISH Engine was also employed for land drainage and the largest such machines were exported to Holland, with the preserved CRUQUIUS Engine being an example of such an installation in the Haarlem Mere. (See page 40).

VENTILATION:

The necessity to provide an adequate source of breathable air in mines was another problem that faced the Mine Captain and, until the middle of the 19th Century, would have been provided by means of natural draught. Adits were utilised for the purpose of ventilation and, in some mines, a second vertical shaft used for winding was sunk to augment natural ventilation. Forced draught by the use of air pumps driven off the pitwork was eventually provided and these in their simplest form were large wooden machines akin to a bicycle pump and placed at intervals down the shaft. The most complex of these ventilation systems was the "Cornish Duck Engine" which was a double-acting piston air pump erected in the engine house and driven from a rod on the beam. A large version of this type of air pump was capable of delivering nearly 90,000 cubic feet of air per hour for distribution in the mine.

THE MAN ENGINE:

This fearsome device was invented in Germany with the first example probably being the unit operated by a water wheel which was installed in 1833 at the SPEGELTHAL MINE in the Harz district. This machine worked to a depth of 110 fathoms, and supplanted the use of ladders which were tiring for the miners after a shift underground.

Cornwall was slow to adopt this form of upward personnel transport and the first of the type was placed in operation under the auspices of the ROYAL CORNWALL POLYTECHNIC SOCIETY in 1842. This trial was only to a shallow depth and it was installed by the TRESAVAEN Adventurers using a water wheel; it was tested successfully in January 1842 to a depth of 24 fathoms and this trial was extended to the 248 fathom level in the following March. The form utilised in Cornwall consisted of small platforms, upon which two men could stand, fitted to the pitwork at intervals corresponding to the stroke of the outdoor side of the beam. Larger sized platforms were attached across the shaft at similar intervals and were placed to coincide with the top and bottom points reached by the pump rod platforms. At the bottom of the stroke the miner would move off the fixed platform in the shaft on to the moving platform on the rod which would then lift him on to the next fixed platform which manoeuvre would be repeated until he had ascended to the top of the shaft. Upon average this action would take about 25 minutes per 1000 ft. which time was about the same as using ladders, but involved far less effort.

In the photograph of the DOLCOATH Man Engine which was started in October 1854 using a 19 in. engine, (Fig. 33), a total of 108 men could be accommodated at any given time. This engine had sollars at either side with the men ascending stepping off at one side and those descending going off at the other. In order to speed up the 25 minute climb and to obviate the pauses, younger men were in the habit of rising one lift and then racing up the ladder to catch the next upward stroke – it all seemed to be perfectly innocuous but given the fact that all of this was done with but the candle-light on the miners' helmets, it was actually fraught with

Fig. 33 - The Dolcoath Mine Man Engine, shown on an angled part of the mine shaft.

danger and a slip meant certain death or injury. In the first month of operation at Dolcoath part of the mechanism broke in two, and fourteen miners travelling on the rod were injured, four of them seriously. By 1865 a total of thirty man-engines were in use in Europe with sixteen being installed in Cornwall, and two at DEVON GREAT CONSOLS (Wheal Josiah and Wheal Emma). The last Man Engine to operate in the United Kingdom was that at LEVANT which worked to a depth of nearly 1500 ft. Unfortunately on the 20th of October 1919 the rod broke near the beam whilst 150 men were on the engine – 31 were killed outright and 11 seriously injured, upon which the use of the machine was terminated.

ANCILLIARY EQUIPMENT:

In waterworks the need to overcome 'pressure pulses' caused by the stroke of the engine which could seriously damage pipework, was met by the erection of large water towers which were in fact vertical reservoirs. The engine pumped the water into the tower and the water stored therein was fed under constant pressure into the mains network. An example of such a tower may be seen at Kew where its use today is to act as a buffer to the 90 inch engine when that machine is demonstrated in steam.

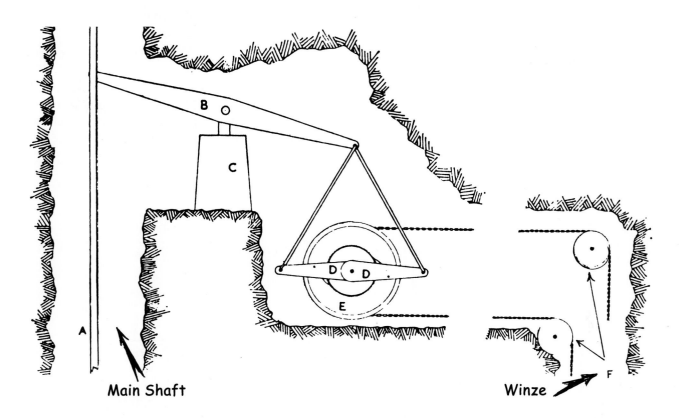

Fig. 34 Schematic drawing of Rowse's machine for raising ore using the pump rod of a Cornish Engine.

Another piece of equipment of interest is *ROWSE's* machine for the raising of ore by the use of a non-rotative engine. This is shown in Fig. 34 where it may be seen as the rod **A** rises and falls it transmits motion to a beam **B** which, in turn, lifts half-beams **D** which turn the winding drum **E** by the use of a ratchet mechanism. Ropes on the winding drum fall over the sheaves **F** to raise or lower kibbles. This winding system was installed at the TYWARNHAILE MINES in 1851 and it was a successful method of converting the linear motion of the pitwork into rotary motion underground. The inventor of this equipment, *ANTHONY ROWSE,* stated that "...although clumsy and, with its ratchets, noisy – it was effective and continued to work until as long as the mine did".

POWER "TAKE-OFFS":

Mine Captains and their engineers were nothing, if not ingenious, and they realised that the inherent vertical motion of the Cornish Engine as harnessed through the Balance Bob could be adapted for use as a 'power take-off' on the horizontal plane. By using rods, usually of flat wood, running over rollers, or some form of pendulum arm, the power could be transmitted for some distance and put to use driving "stamps" (ore-crushing machines), pumps in other shafts, winding drums as mentioned above, and so on. By utilising the Balance Bob for such purposes it enabled the mine engineers to avoid purchasing a separate 'whim' (rotative) engine to do these jobs.

APPENDIX A - Drawings of Crofton No. 1 Boulton & Watt Engine

These drawings which are reproduced by kind permission of *R. SIMMONS* Esq. of the CROFTON SOCIETY show the layout of the Cornish Valve gear as applied to the No 1 Engine at Crofton after it was rebuilt to operate on the Cornish Cycle by HARVEY & Co. of Hayle in 1845 (See Page 38). Also included is a Pressure Diagram for the engine as well as sections etc of the cylinder head and piston.

1 - Bottom: The Boulton & Watt 36" engine as installed in 1809.

2 - Left: The Sims Combined Engine incorporating a double cylinder (one on top of the other) which was installed at Crofton in 1846.

3 - Below: The Sims Double Cylinder arrangement.

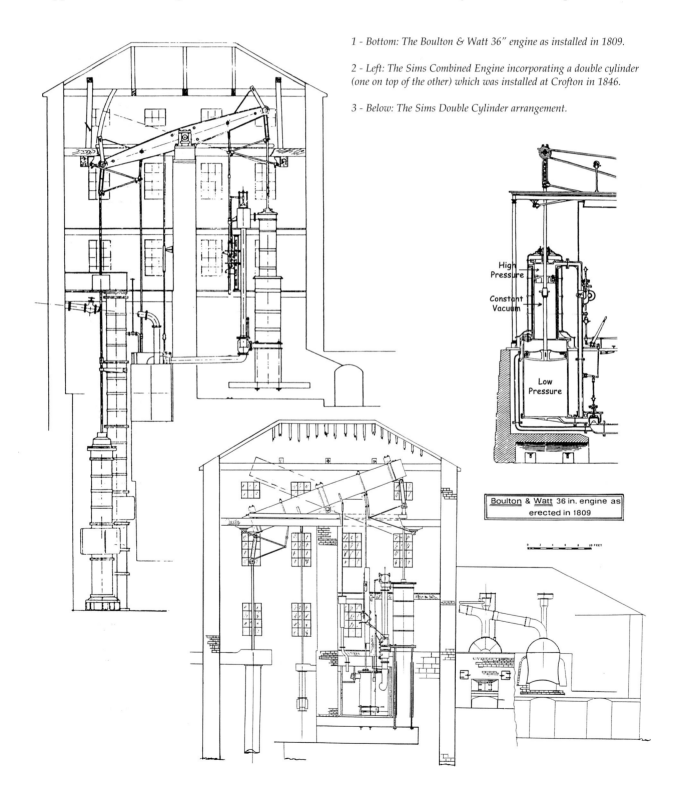

Boulton & Watt 36 in. engine as erected in 1809

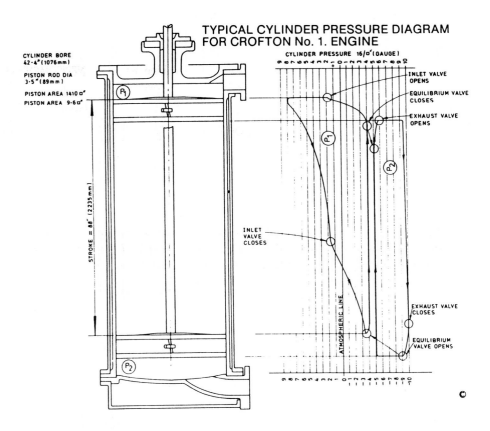

TYPICAL CYLINDER PRESSURE DIAGRAM
FOR CROFTON No. 1. ENGINE

CYLINDER BORE
42·4″ (1076mm)

PISTON ROD DIA
3·5″ (89mm)

PISTON AREA 1410 □″
PISTON AREA 9·6 □″

STROKE = 88″ (2235mm)

CYLINDER PRESSURE 16/0″ (GAUGE)

INLET VALVE OPENS
EQUILIBRIUM VALVE CLOSES
EXHAUST VALVE OPENS

INLET VALVE CLOSES

EXHAUST VALVE CLOSES

EQUILIBRIUM VALVE OPENS

ATMOSPHERIC LINE

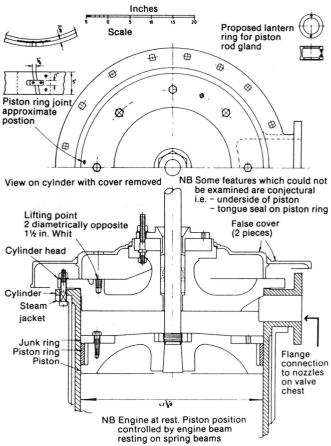

Inches
Scale

Proposed lantern ring for piston rod gland

Piston ring joint approximate postion

View on cylnder with cover removed

NB Some features which could not be examined are conjectural
i.e. – underside of piston
– tongue seal on piston ring

Lifting point 2 diametrically opposite 1½ in. Whit

Cylinder head

Cylinder Steam jacket

Junk ring
Piston ring
Piston

False cover (2 pieces)

Flange connection to nozzles on valve chest

NB Engine at rest. Piston position controlled by engine beam resting on spring beams

**CROFTON No. 1 ENGINE CYLINDER
HEAD & PISTON**

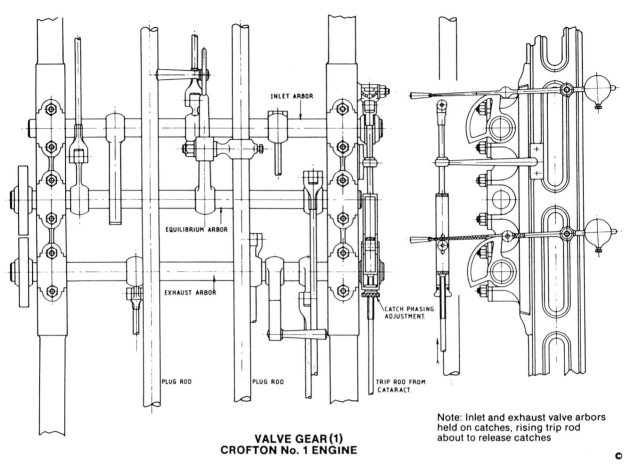

VALVE GEAR (1)
CROFTON No. 1 ENGINE

Note: Inlet and exhaust valve arbors held on catches, rising trip rod about to release catches

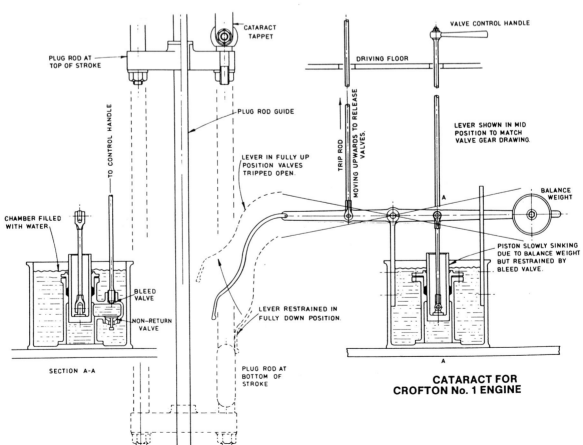

CATARACT FOR
CROFTON No. 1 ENGINE

Engine at rest at top of stroke
equilibrium valve closed by tappet
quadrant clear to allow exhaust to open
engine waiting for trip rod to rise
and release catches to allow
inlet and exhaust valves to open

A

Inlet and exhaust valves open
engine on its way down "in house"
stroke.
Equilibrium valve restrained
by quadrant

B

Engine at bottom of stroke
inlet already shut by tappet.
Tappet has shut exhaust valve
Equilibrium arbor released by
quadrant and has rotated to open valve
engine about to return "out of house"

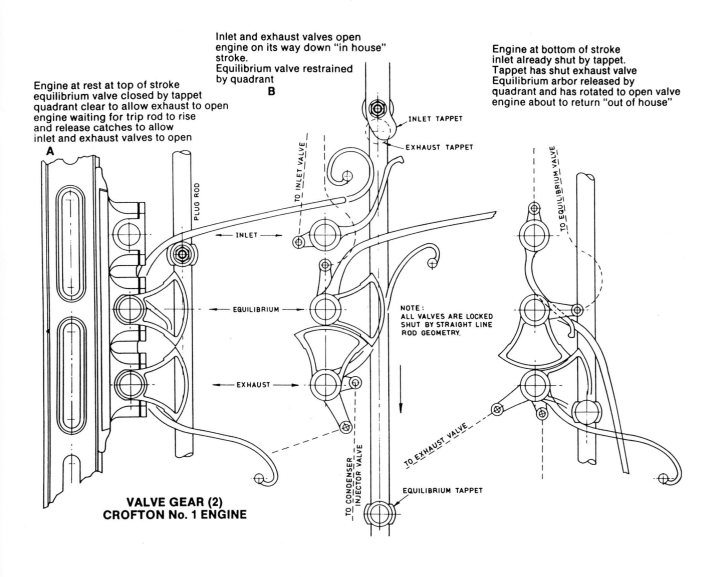

INLET TAPPET

EXHAUST TAPPET

TO INLET VALVE

INLET

EQUILIBRIUM

EXHAUST

TO EQUILIBRIUM VALVE

NOTE:
ALL VALVES ARE LOCKED
SHUT BY STRAIGHT LINE
ROD GEOMETRY.

PLUG ROD

**VALVE GEAR (2)
CROFTON No. 1 ENGINE**

TO CONDENSER
INJECTOR VALVE

TO EXHAUST VALVE

EQUILIBRIUM TAPPET

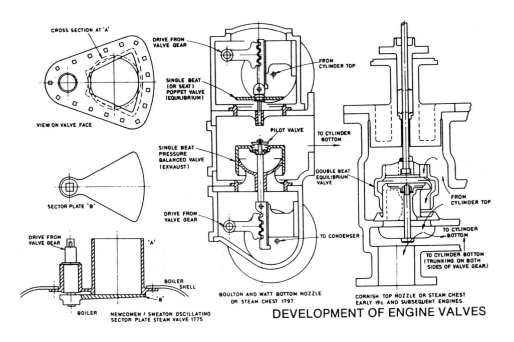

CROSS SECTION AT 'A'

DRIVE FROM
VALVE GEAR

FROM
CYLINDER TOP

SINGLE BEAT
(OR SEAT)
POPPET VALVE
(EQUILIBRIUM)

VIEW ON VALVE FACE

SINGLE BEAT
PRESSURE
BALANCED VALVE
(EXHAUST)

PILOT VALVE

TO CYLINDER
BOTTOM

DOUBLE BEAT
EQUILIBRIUM
VALVE

SECTOR PLATE 'B'

DRIVE FROM
VALVE GEAR

FROM
CYLINDER TOP

DRIVE FROM
VALVE GEAR

'A'

TO CONDENSER

TO CYLINDER
BOTTOM

BOILER
SHELL

'B'

TO CYLINDER BOTTOM
(TRUNKING ON BOTH
SIDES OF VALVE GEAR)

BOILER

NEWCOMEN / SMEATON OSCILLATING
SECTOR PLATE STEAM VALVE 1775.

BOULTON AND WATT BOTTOM NOZZLE
OR STEAM CHEST 1797.

CORNISH TOP NOZZLE OR STEAM CHEST
EARLY 19c. AND SUBSEQUENT ENGINES.

DEVELOPMENT OF ENGINE VALVES

Appendix B - The Restoration of the 70 inch Bull Pumping Engine at Kew Bridge Steam Museum

The Bull Engine Restoration Committee was created in January 1999 to formulate proposals to return the BULL engine (See Fig. 13 - Page 32) into working order in the same condition as it was at the time of its de-commissioning in 1945. This group is composed entirely of Members of the *KEW BRIDGE ENGINES TRUST* and the objectives behind the restoration are to provide finance, expertise and labour over a three-year period to achieve a fully working exhibit. Following a detailed survey of the machinery and its surroundings, the total cost of the project was estimated at £72000, which included a notional volunteer labour input set at £38000.

The restoration was commenced in February 2001 and was assisted by an award of £12000 from the Science Museum PRISM Fund and a further sum of £14500 from the National Heritage Fund.

This engine is one of three survivors of the BULL pattern that are known to exist and it is the only one remaining in its original location; all three of these BULL engines were manufactured by Messrs. Harvey & Co. of Hayle in Cornwall. The *KEW BRIDGE* example is the largest of the three machines having a 70-inch cylinder bore; it was built in the years of 1856 and 1857 and it was installed into the original Georgian Engine House at Kew in 1859. Its prime purpose was the delivery of fresh water to the GRAND JUNCTION WATERWORKS Co. high-level reservoirs at Campden Hill, near Notting Hill Gate in London. In actual fact the engine appears to have been only used for standby purposes whenever one of the large Cornish engines was out of service, for its valve gear shows little signs of wear. The other two existing BULL engines are both 50-inch units which were supplied to pump out the SEVERN TUNNEL, being built in the years of 1876 and 1877.

Work on the engine has progressed well, for many of the components were found to be in remarkably good condition. In October 2001 the piston was moved for the first time in 57 years and, using hydraulic power, it was raised about 8 inches on several occasions; steady progress has been made with the removal of some major parts for cleaning and refurbishment. These items included the cataract mechanism, the rocking beam that drives the air-pump together with the plug rod and the suction and delivery valves. The asbestos lagging has been removed and this is being replaced with 'Rockwool' for insulation around the cylinder wall etc. Now that the piston has been freed off, it will be possible to move it upwards to its fullest extent, so that access to the pump gland will be afforded in order to renovate it; the original doorway between the engine houses containing the MAUDSLAY and the BULL engines has been re-instated, using the original doors so that transferral of large items is an easier proposition. Some new items have already been purchased at the time of writing, and these comprise a length of 8 inch steam pipe and a set of six square-thread studs complete with nuts that have been machined by John Viner.

The Bull Engine Restoration Committee Secretary, Mr. N. Morgan, who took the writer on a tour of the BULL site, explained that some deliberations had to be made regarding the final colour scheme to be employed on both engine and engine house. Some of the items removed so far reveal green paint but there are also traces of red together with a red ochre found on the surrounding walls. This red pigment may date from the early 1990s and investigations into colour selection are ongoing.

A fund has been set up to assist with financing the project and this is open to public contribution; further details may be obtained from the Museum.

Specifications of the BULL Pumping Engine:

Cylinder Bore & Stroke	– 70 inch by 10 ft. (1770 x 3040 mm)
Pump Diameter & Stroke	– 28 inch by 10 ft. (711 x 3040 mm)
Pump Delivery per stroke	– 236 Imp. Gallons (1071 litres)
Steam Pressure	– 40p.s.i. (2.8Kg.cm^2)

APPENDIX C - Table of Observations upon Ten Cornish Engines by John S. Enys Esq. Recorded in 1838

			CONSOLIDATED MINES.						UNITED MINES.			
			Taylor's engine.	Davy's engine.[1]	Job's engine.[2]	Woolf's engine.[3]	Bawden's engine.[4]	Pearce's engine.	Cardozo's engine.[5]	Eldon's engine.[6]	Loam's engine.[7]	Hocking's engine.
Dimensions of engine.	Diameter of cylinder	in inches.	85	80	65	90	90	65	90	30	85	85
	Stroke of piston	in feet.	10	$11\frac{1}{3}$	9	10	10	9	9	9	10	10
	Diameter of steam valve	in inches.	12	13	9	8	8	7	10	5	10	12
	,, equilibrium valve	,,	16	18	12	16	16	12	13	7	16	16
	,, exhaustion valve	,,	20	24	14	19	19	14	15	10	19	19
Dimensions of boilers.	Number of boilers		4	3	2	4	3	3	3	1	3	3
	Length of boilers	in feet.	{3·36 1·40}	37	{31 32}	35	36	36	36	36	{1·32 2·38}	44
	Diameter of boilers	,,	$6\frac{1}{2}$	7	$6\frac{1}{2}$	$6\frac{1}{4}$	$6\frac{1}{4}$	$6\frac{1}{4}$	$6\frac{1}{4}$	$6\frac{1}{2}$	$6\frac{1}{2}$	$6\frac{1}{2}$
	,, tubes	,,	{3·$3\frac{3}{4}$ 1·4}	$4\frac{1}{3}$	$3\frac{3}{4}$	$3\frac{3}{4}$	$3\frac{3}{4}$	$3\frac{3}{4}$	$3\frac{3}{4}$	4	4	4
	Length of fire bars	,,	4	4	4	4	4	4	4	4	4	4
	Total area of fire bars	,,	63	52	30	60	45	45	48	16	48	48
	Heating surface exposed to flues	,,	3781	3151	1598	3481	2694	2694	2694	941	2952	3451
	Water space	in cub. ft.	2467	2025	1033	2140	1650	1650	1650	579	1706	2085
	Steam space	,,	735	580	315	608	468	468	468	178	528	645
Tempera-tures ob-served.	Open air	Fahrenheit.	57°	57°	..	57°	57°	51°	55°	56°	51°	55°
	Engine-house	,,	..	..	..	..	..	67°	..	55°	63°	66°
	Ashes over boiler	,,	80°	80°	81°	98°	98°	97°	88°	99°	79°	82°
	Cylinder cover	,,	111°	90°	102°	126°	96°	109°	94°	98°	90°	84°
	Middle of cylinder clothing *	,,	W 77°	W 76°	B 95°	B 102°	B 140°	..	B 79°	W 60°	W 67°	W 68°
	Clothing of steam pipe	,,	79°	..	..	130°	95°	..	140°	97°	80°	82°
	Condensing water	,,	64°	84°	58°	115°	110°	57°	60°	61°	63°	60°
	Hot well	,,	98°	100°	91°	140°	140°	97°	104°	94°	102°	96°
	Height of condenser barometer	in inches.	$27\frac{1}{4}$	$27\frac{1}{2}$	..	$25\frac{1}{2}$	..	..	..	..	..	$27\frac{1}{2}$
	Number of plunger pumps		9	12	2	7	8	9	8	1	5	5
	,, bucket pumps		2	2	..	1	2	2	2	..	4	3
	Water load per square inch of piston	in lbs.	11·46	13·12	8·78	11·56	8·3	16·8	11·5	17·96	11·95	13·58
	Proportion of stroke where steam cut off		$\frac{1}{5}$	$\frac{1}{5}$	..	$\frac{1}{3}$	$\frac{1}{3}$	$\frac{1}{4}$	$\frac{1}{3}$	$\frac{1}{3}$	$\frac{2}{11}$	..
	Strokes per minute		$8\frac{1}{2}$	$7\frac{1}{2}$	..	9	9	10	$8\frac{1}{2}$	9	8	7
	Proportion of duration of in-door to out-door stroke		4 : 7	5 : 8	4 : 7	5 : 7	5 : 7	5 : 6	4 : $6\frac{1}{2}$	4 : 7	1 : 2	4 : $7\frac{1}{2}$
	Grease used per day	in lbs.	12	12	10	12	12	10	12	6	12	12
	Oil used per day	in pints.	1	1	1	1	1	1	1	$\frac{1}{2}$	1	1
	Men employed		4	4	3	4	4	3	4	3	4	4
	Boys employed		3	3	3	4	4	3	3	..	3	3

[1] Six years old. The show engine of the mine. [2] Employed in raising water 47 fathoms for the wheels and injection. [3] Cylinder in bad condition, since changed.
[4] Old engine. 1820. [5] Old engine; no steam jacket. [6] Old engine refitted. [7] An old 90-inch cylinder used for the steam jacket of this engine.
* The prefix of the letter B signifies that the casing is of brick; and W, of wood.

BIBLIOGRAPHY

1) BOOKS

"A Treatise on the Steam Engine"
– JOHN FAREY. Longmans, London. 1827.
Re-printed by David & Charles, Newton Abbot. 1971.

"A Descriptive History of the Steam Engine"
– R. STUART. Knight & Lacey, London. 1828

"The Steam Engine" – TREDGOLD. London. 1828

"On the Steam Engines in Cornwall"
– THOMAS LEAN. Simpkin, Marshall, London. 1839. *Re-printed D. Bradford Barton, Truro. 1969*

"Treatise on the Cornish Pumping Engine"
– WILLIAM POLE. Weale of High Holborn. 1844

"Lives of Boulton & Watt"
- SAMUEL SMILES. Murray, London. 1865

"History of the Growth of the Steam Engine"
– THURSTON. C. Kegan, Paul & Co., London. 1880

"The Steam Engine & It's Inventors"
– R. L. GALLOWAY. Macmillan, London. 1881

"A Text Book on Steam & Steam Engines"
– ANDREW JAMIESON. Charles Griffin & Co., London. 1886

"Steam Engine Theory & Practice"
– WILLIAM RIPPER. Longmans, London. 1899

"James Watt & the Steam Engine"
– H. W. DICKINSON & R. JENKINS.
Clarendon Press, London. 1927.
Re-printed Encore Editions, London. 1981

"Richard Trevithick, The Engineer & The Man"
– H. W. DICKINSON & A. TITLEY. London. 1934

"Thomas Newcomen, The Pre-history of the Steam Engine"
– L. T. C. ROLT. David & Charles, London. 1963

"The Cornish Giant"
– L. T. C. ROLT. Lutterworth Press. 1960

"The Cornish Beam Engine"
– D. BRADFORD BARTON.
D. Bradford Barton, Truro. 1965

"James Watt & the Steam Revolution"
– E. ROBINSON & A. E. MUSSON. Adams & Dart, London. 1969

"Arthur Woolf, the Cornish Engineer"
– T. R. HARRIS. D. Bradford Barton, Truro. 1969

"The Newcomen Engine in the West of England"
– K. H. ROGERS. Moonraker Press, Bradford-upon-Avon. 1976

"The Steam Engine of Thomas Newcomen"
– L. T. C. ROLT & J. S. ALLEN. Moorland Publishing Co., Hartington. 1977

"The Steam Engine in Industry"
– GEORGE WATKINS. Moorland Publishing Co., Ashbourne. 1979

"Cornish Beam Engines in South Australian mines"
– G. J. DREW & J. E. CONNELL. Department of Mines and Energy, South Australia. 1993

"Water Supply of Greater London"
– H. W. DICKINSON. The Newcomen Society. 1954

2) BOOKLETS

"Cornish Pumping Engines"
– Cornish Engines Preservation Society, Redruth. 1953. *Reprinted under the auspices of the TREVITHICK SOCIETY with additions in 1985, 1991 & 1998.*

"Boulton, Watt & the Soho Undertakings"
– W. K. V. GALE F.R.Hist.S. Museum of Science & Industry, Birmingham.

"The Steam Engine"
– R. J. LAW B.Sc. H. M. S. O., London. 1965

"James Watt & the Separate Condenser"
– R. J. LAW B.Sc.. H. M. S. O., London. 1969

"Cornish Engines and Engine Houses"

– PETER LAWS. The National Trust, London. 1973

"Crofton Beam Engines – A Guided Tour"
"Crofton Beam Engines – The Story of Crofton Pumping Station on the Kennet & Avon Canal"
– both DAVID HARRIS. The Crofton Society, 1975

"Steam Power – An Illustrated Guide"
– G. WATKINS & F. WIGHTMAN.
David & Charles, Newton Abbot. 1982

"Thomas Newcomen – Engineer 1663/4 to 1729"
– H. W. DICKINSON (1929). *Revised by P. RUSSELL F.S.A. 1952. J. S. ALLEN & J.G. B. HILLS 1975 and J. S. ALLEN 1979 & 1989.* The Newcomen Society. 1989

"Cornish Engines & the Men who Handled Them"
– J. H. TROUNSON. The Trevithick Society, Redruth. 1992

"Cornwall's Old Mines"
– H. V. WILLIAMS . Tor Mark Press, Truro.

"A Guide to Kew Bridge Steam Museum"
– JOHN GUY. Hephaistos Publishing Ltd. 1989

"Cornish Engine Houses"
– Tor Mark Press, Truro. 1999

3) TRADE CATALOGUES

HARVEY'S HAYLE FOUNDRY – 1884. *Re-printed by D. Bradford Barton, Truro. 1973*

WILLIAMS' PERRAN FOUNDRY Co. – c.1879
Re-printed by the Trevithick Society, Redruth. 1974

4) LEARNED JOURNALS Etc.

The TRANSACTIONS of the NEWCOMEN SOCIETY (Various)

The TREVITHICK SOCIETY JOURNAL (Various)

"The Newcomen Engine"
– H. DAVEY. Proceedings of the Institute of Mechanical Engineers Oct./Dec. 1903

"The MODEL ENGINEER"
"The Non-Rotative Beam Engine"
– ROY SIMMONS. 18th May to 2nd August 1990.

"Crofton – The Cornish Influence & James Sims"
– R. SIMMONS. *UNPUBLISHED*